Japanese
Quality
Concepts

An Overview

Japanese Quality Concepts

An Overview

Katsuya Hosotani

QUALITY RESOURCES
A Division of The Kraus Organization Limited
White Plains, New York

Published by
  Quality Resources
  A Division of The Kraus Organization Limited
  One Water Street
  White Plains, NY 10601

Manufactured in the United States of America

96 95 94 93 92   5 4 3 2 1

The paper used in this publication meets the minimum requirements of American National Standard for Information Sciences—Permanence of Paper for Printed Library Materials, ANSI Z39.48-1984.

ISBN 0-527-91651-X

Library of Congress Cataloging-in-Publication Data
Hosotani, Katsuya, 1938–
   [QC-teki mono no mikata, kangaekata. English]
   Japanese quality concepts : an overview / Katsuya Hosotani.
     p. cm.
   Translation of: QC-teki mono no mikata, kangaekata.
   Includes bibliographical references and index.
   ISBN 0-527-91651-X
   1. Total quality management—Japan. I. Title.
HD62.15.H6713 1992   92-12106
658.5′62′0952—dc20   CIP

Contents

Preface

It is no secret that TQC (total quality control) activities play a very important role in many companies in Japan and have met with great success. Interest in Japanese TQC is growing in foreign countries as well, since it is seen as the reason for the superior products that Japanese companies manufacture. And manufacturing is not the only sector that has experienced increasing use of TQC: other industries, such as construction, the service industry, and the financial industry, are also implementing TQC.

The role TQC has played in new-product development is not the only reason it has had such great success. It has also spurred improvements in company organization, initiated workplace activities, and brought about an awareness of company objectives, all rationally focused on quality control. The essence of TQC is "the QC attitude and point of view."

Through the great efforts of many dedicated teachers, this rational and scientific way of thinking has been persistently introduced into industry's education and training. The necessity of implementing TQC has been emphasized in the field of quality control throughout the country. This means that companies implementing it can do so confidently.

The author has been advocating a QC attitude and point of view, and his thoughts were summarized and published three years ago in the magazine *Quality Monthly* (No. 129). The work was well received and has been reissued every year since then. At the urging of the publisher, it has been rewritten and revised and has resulted in the present book. The book is organized in 20 topics such as quality first, the PDCA cycle, focusing on priorities, fact-based management, focusing on the customer, process control, and using QC techniques.

The book has been arranged for use by top management and department heads, as well as staff. Its content is presented in a form that is easy to comprehend, and it gives specifics that will allow companies to achieve a thorough understanding of what TQC is and how it can be promoted.

The interpretations herein are based on the author's own observations and opinions. Any comments from readers are welcome—they will help to improve a later version of this book.

For a company to survive in the increasingly harsh international environment, creative and internationally competitive products and services with improved cost reduction and with quality that meets worldwide needs are vital. The author will be happy if this book is helpful in promoting TQC in companies that are looking to meet the challenges of tomorrow's marketplace.

My deepest appreciation goes to my teachers, T. Asaka, K. Ishikawa, S. Mizuno, Y. Kondo, and others in the field of QC for their teaching and their advice over a long period of time, and for giving me permission to use their references and experiences. My thanks also go to those at JUSE Press for their help in the publication of this book, particularly to H. Mitsuaki, K. Nio, and C. Takehana.

K. Hosotani
September 1984
Kobe Kokusai Kaikan
QC Circle Kinki Branch
20th Anniversary Conference

How to Read and Apply This Book

This book is designed for those implementing TQC. We summarize here the basics of TQC implementation, that is, QC attitude, point of view, and promotion. It has been written for companywide introduction of QC awareness and for further promotion of TQC activities. It can also be used by a company for in-house education of its people.

ORGANIZATION OF THE BOOK

Table 1 presents a classification of the 20 chapters into five categories. Each chapter includes the following three points:

1. *Explanation of terms*—Terms are defined, and the QC attitude and point of view are explained.

2. *Effective promotion*—A summary of the effects of implementation along with procedures, crucial points, and precautions for effective implementation.

3. *Practical examples*—Examples are selected from experiences by Deming Prize recipient companies and other companies that have applied TQC successfully.

TO THE READER

This book has been arranged for readers in top management, those who are department heads and staff, and also for a broad range of readers in other areas of an organization.

TABLE 1. QC attitude and point of view.

Classification	QC Attitude and Point of View
T Total	(1) Strengthening company quality (2) Management with participation by everyone (16) Education (19) The QC audit (20) Respecting others
S Statistical	(10) Using QC techniques (13) Control of variation
Q QA	(3) Quality first (8) Focusing on the customer (9) The next step in the process is your customer
C Control	(4) The PDCA cycle (6) Fact-based management (7) Process control (12) Standardization (15) Upstream control (17) Policy control (18) Cross-functional management
I Improvement	(5) Focusing on priorities (11) Problem-solving procedures (14) Preventing recurring and potential problems

Note: Numbers in parentheses indicate chapter numbers.

- *Top management*—Your role is to provide leadership and to emphasize TQC by understanding the various roles, attitudes, and promotions.

- *Department heads*—Your role is to assume responsibility and to understand areas of TQC such as policy control and consumer orientation, as well as the methods for basic promotion of TQC.

- *Staff*—Your role is to achieve a solid understanding of TQC and to implement the specifics.

- *QC circle leaders and members*—Your role is to understand the QC point of view in order to produce high-quality products and services at less cost, more quickly, more easily, and more safely, and to learn about control and improvement.

Thus, TQC is an activity participated in by everyone, and so the contents of this book need to be understood by all members of a company.

This book is also ideally suited for those people who wish to introduce TQC but are uncertain of the methods of introducing it, those promoting

TABLE 2. One-day course.

	9 a.m.–12 a.m.	*1 p.m.–5 p.m.*
1st Day	QC attitude and point of view (1) (Chapters 1–10)	QC attitude and point of view (2) (Chapters 11–20)

TQC but faced with impediments or suffering from slow progress, and those aiming for a Deming Prize and working hard to establish TQC.

HOW TO USE THE BOOK

This book can be used in the following ways:

- Use it as a text for in-house meetings or other study groups.

   Tables 2 and 3 give sample curricula for meetings using this book. Such a meeting can be adapted into a two-day course, which we recommend, and is ideal for learning the basic concepts of TQC and how to promote it. If the seminar is in a hotel setting, the evening of the first day can be used for group discussion.

   If only one day is available for this training, you could emphasize the meanings of the terms and how to promote TQC and review the practical examples, which can then be self-taught by the members. We also recommend for staff-level people that they read books such as *7 QC Tools, Practice of Easy QC Methods*, by K. Hosotani (JUSE Press, 1982) and *Introduction to Statistical Methods for QC*, by K. Kurogane (JUSE Press, 1977) for additional material on QC methodology.

- This book can be used as a secondary text or reference book in another course.

- It can be used as a manual to tackle specific problems in the practice of TQC activities.

TABLE 3. Two-day course.

	9 a.m.–12 a.m.	*1 p.m.–5 p.m.*
1st Day	Overview of TQC (Chapters 1–3)	Basics and promotion of TQC (1) (Chapters 4–10)
2nd Day	Basics and promotion of TQC (2) (Chapters 11–16)	Subsystems of TQC (Chapters 17–20)

HOW TO READ THE BOOK

The following points are important.

1. Start with Chapter 1 and read the chapters in order. Chapters 1 through 10 are of particular importance.
2. Select chapters of particular interest.

HOW TO TEACH

The following points are important.

- Run an in-company seminar. Call in QC experts from outside the company to use as teachers if possible, or use experienced in-house people.
- Include group discussions in the study meetings and ask people to read portions in turn.
- Study alone.

The ways to use and read this book have been described, but what is most important is implementing TQC. From practice comes new experience and correct understanding.

1

Strengthening Company Quality

The purpose of this chapter is to show how to use total quality control to strengthen the organizational structure of a company and thus assure continuing prosperity.

WHAT IS TQC?

The business objective of an enterprise is to contribute to the well-being of society by performing necessary activities that fulfill demands for a certain product or service within its market area. A company cannot justify its presence unless it is able to offer a needed product or service at the proper price, in the time required, and delivered to the place required. If it cannot do so, it is unable to compete effectively.

What is quality control? It is setting a quality target for a company that assures the quality that is required by the customers—not only the quality specified, but quality in a broad sense that includes function, product life, economy of use, safety, and service—and achieving it rationally and economically.

QC Terminology (JIS Z 8101) of the Japan Industrial Standards defines quality control as follows:

Quality control—A system or means to produce economically products or services with a quality that matches the buyer's requirements.
   Quality control is often abbreviated as QC.
   Because of the adoption of statistical methods in quality control, it is often called ''statistical quality control'' (SQC). To implement QC effectively, the participation and cooperation of all members of the company, from manag-

1

ers, controllers, and supervisors to the workers, are necessary throughout all stages of market research, R&D, product planning, design, production planning, purchasing and outsourcing, production, inspection, sales, after-service, finance, personnel, and education. Implementing QC in this fashion is also called "companywide quality control" (CWQC) or "total quality control" (TQC).

As is clear from this JIS definition, TQC has the following three aspects.

The Meaning of TQC

1. *Performed at every stage of the operation.* There are several steps involved in offering products and services that please one's customers. These steps include market needs that are researched and products that are planned, designed, produced, sold, and later serviced. A means of quality assurance should be established so that each one of these steps can be fulfilled.

2. *Participation by everyone in every department.* Quality control needs to be implemented by every individual who participates in the corporation. This means the president, vice-president, department and section managers, group heads, staff, and supervisors. Good products cannot be made if some of the departments or sections believe that they do not have a role in quality control. General administration and personnel departments as well should be required to study QC and to execute their functions by implementing quality control.

3. *Organizing implementation.* Although controlling quality is the center of activities, parallel progress in control of cost (profit price), volume (production, sales, inventory), delivery (process control), safety, and human resources (education, training) is necessary. The level of control can be upgraded and can produce products that are desirable and satisfying to the consumer. This concept is simply expressed in Figure 1.1.

JIS uses the term CWQC, rather than TQC. This is because TQC was first used by Dr. A.V. Feigenbaum of the United States, who in 1957 presented a paper entitled "Total Quality Control." In it he said that TQC is an effective system that encompasses the efforts of quality development, quality maintenance, and quality improvement by each group within an organization. This results in more economical production and service that takes into consideration customer satisfaction. He advocated also that QC needed to be performed at all stages that are, by necessity, centered on the QC engineers. On the other hand, we say that quality control needs to be performed not only by some parts of an organization, but by everybody, at all stages, in all departments. This is the Japanese definition of TQC. Since outside of Japan

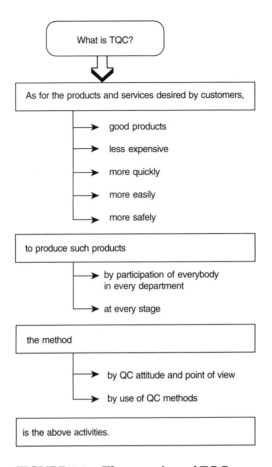

FIGURE 1.1.   The meaning of TQC.

TQC tends to be associated with Dr. Feigenbaum's definition, the term CWQC was introduced in Japan to replace TQC.

Recently, though, we are seeing in Japan that the expression "Japanese TQC" is used more often than CWQC to indicate companywide quality control, and that is the style followed in this book.

DEVELOPMENT AND HISTORY OF QUALITY CONTROL

Here is a brief history of quality control in Japan.

Period 1—QC study and research, 1945–49. After the end of World War II, U.S. wartime specifications Z1.1-1.3 were introduced in this country by the military government of the allied forces. Because we were looking to restore our industries, a quality control research group was started on the basis of these specifications plus some reference materials on statistical methods. This took place in 1946.

In 1945, Japan Standards Association (JSA) and, in 1946, the Union of Japanese Scientists and Engineers (JUSE) were established. During this time W.G. Mcgill and H.M. Sarason of the GHQ were conducting quality control guidance training for electrical equipment manufacturers. In 1949, quality control seminars were started by JUSE and the Nikkikyo which have continued to the present.

In 1946, an Industry Standardization Law was enacted and the JIS mark was established for display on products.

Period 2—Introduction of SQC and its popularization, 1950–54. Dr. W.E. Deming visited Japan in 1950 and put on an eight-day seminar. The course was of epoch-making importance in the development of QC in this country because it gave direction to the introduction and the use of statistical methods to many people involved with manufacturing. The Deming Prize was established in 1951.

The First QC Conference was held in November 1951, and such conferences have continued to be held each November since then. At these conferences, the results of research and examples of administration and improvement are presented.

Other QC seminars were arranged by JUSE and the JSA to learn new methods. This was a period that centered around inspection, and statistical methods were used for inspection at the time of receiving raw materials, during the process, and at the final inspection.

In 1954, Dr. J.M. Juran visited Japan to give seminars, and this was a turning point in emphasizing quality control for management.

Period 3—Organization administration of quality control and emphasis on process control, 1955–59. In 1955, Japan underwent what has become known as the Jimmu-boom, which saw the economy of Japan develop in an orderly fashion. In 1956, Japan along with the United States experienced a recession but soon recovered, and the next period was known as the Iwato-boom. (Jimmu and Iwato are the names of legendary Japanese leaders.)

In the world of quality control, QC functions within a company were organized and permanent QC promotion groups such as committees, QC promotion offices, and QA departments were established. Also at this time, QC education for management, supervisors, and clerical departments was started. QC seminars were broadcast on radio and TV, which contributed to its popular appeal.

In 1958, the First Standardization National Conference was held, and since then October and November of every year have come to be known as the industrial standardization promotion period, during which dissemination and promotion of industrial standardization takes place. Since quality cannot be maintained merely by inspection, the concept of building quality into the process began to be considered.

Period 4—QC activities enhancing the shop floor, 1960–64. The development and popularization of quality control occurred rapidly. November of every year has been set aside as quality month since 1960. This is a time when QC self-reflection, diagnosis, and promotion are performed by various companies, and there is a movement to make this a national effort.

Dr. Feigenbaum published his book *Total Quality Control* in 1961, and a management conference was included as part of the QC conferences.

In 1962, QC circles were advocated and a foremen's conference was added to the QC conference in November of that year. In addition, QC activities for the plant were also promoted.

Period 5—Japanese quality control, 1965–69. Japan was experiencing again a period of rapid economic growth, and this was called the Izanagi-boom, when Japan's GNP became the second largest in the free world. Also at this time the Basic Laws for Pollution were established, and protection of the environment as well as consumer protection began to attract attention.

As production increased in scale so did the investment of capital. And so setting up high-quality production and manufacturing with high efficiency and low cost became more important. During this period also Japanese quality control began to attract worldwide attention.

In 1967, the first QS (QC and standardization) National Conference was held. This continues to be held every May, and is a time when industry and academic professionals make presentations and hold discussions that contribute to the promotion and popularization of TQC.

As communication overseas began to intensify, QC groups were sent abroad every year and the world's first International QC Conference was held in Tokyo in 1969.

Period 6—Quality assurance and reliability, 1970–74. The period of high economic growth in Japan ended with the Nixon shock of 1971 and the oil crisis of 1973.

As a result of free trade, concern about product defects in automobiles, microwave ovens, and prefab housing, as well as about countermeasures against our continually expanding market share, has brought about further interest in QC at every stage of a business. This includes investigation of consumer demands, research, design, production, sales, and after-service, and all of these are now emphasized in industries' attitudes toward quality assurance (QA) and reliability.

Also emphasized was the prevention of product liability (PL) problems, and experts from the United States were called in to give seminars in 1973 for us to study and then implement corrective action. In 1974, the Ministry of Welfare published a draft for good manufacturing practices

(GMP), and, in 1975, voluntary regulation of QC in medical products was promoted.

Period 7—Improving industrial organization structure, 1975–79. In 1976, the strength of the yen made energy and resource conservation a high social priority. Industry was suddenly faced with a severe situation that it had never experienced before. In 1980, the Industrial Standardization Law was revised, and the JIS (Japanese Industrial Standards) mark was opened to application by foreign companies.

During this time, QC was introduced and promoted throughout industry, and many companies began looking to apply QC companywide and to achieve total functional efficiency in their activities.

Period 8—Internationalization of TQC, 1980–present. Trade friction and a decrease in purchasing power have surfaced. At the same time, we see a diversification of quality demands, consumerism, and the popularization of microcomputers and robots. This has brought a period of uncertainty, both socially and economically.

To cope with these conditions, enhancement of the management structure through TQC and paring down of management have been trends not only in the manufacturing industries but also in service industries such as construction, banking, trading companies, hotels, and restaurants.

Also at this time, the superiority of Japanese products that are exported because of free trade began to be recognized and Japanese quality control, which has given birth to these products, has begun to attract international attention. Japan has started to receive study groups of trainees and students from overseas who have come to study quality control in Japan.

Industry in our country must proceed along the path of international coexistence and co-prosperity, and must broaden its international point of view, particularly regarding the problems of international trade friction. This is being accomplished by local production abroad and international sharing of work.

THE GOALS OF INTRODUCING TQC

A survey of six large companies that received the Deming Implementation Prize in 1982 and 1983 was taken to determine their reasons for introducing TQC. The results are shown in Table 1.1, which shows that "strengthening the company organization" is the number one target. The Deming Prize is an award given to companies or business divisions that recognizes their implementation of QC and the outstanding results. This award is considered to be the most honored quality control award in Japan. It was established in 1951 to commemorate the work and the friendship of Dr. W.E. Deming, who has contributed so much to the introduction of QC in Japan. The award is also

TABLE 1.1. Aim of TQC introduction at Deming Prize recipient companies.

No.	Company	Aim of TQC introduction	Award Year
1	Kajima Corp.	To build a healthy company structure that assures continued growth	1982
2	Nippon Electric Yamagata, Ltd.	Improvement of company structure by TQC introduction	1982
3	Yokogawa–Hewlett Packard (HP) Co., Ltd.	1. Establishment of QC system 2. Improvement of control structure 3. Positive cooperation with HP	1982
4	Rhythm Watch Co., Ltd.	To build the company structure by promotion of total participation; production of world-class products for contribution to society	1982
5	Shimizu Corp.	Sales activities stressing quality; reformed consciousness	1983
6	Japan Steel Works, Ltd.	1. Resilience to changes in business environment; actualizing a revolutionary business structure 2. Achieving customer satisfaction and trust while maintaining or increasing profitability	1983

important in further developing quality control, so it is given to companies and their divisions that have been recognized for outstanding results in their implementation of quality principles.

HOW TO STRENGTHEN ORGANIZATIONAL STRUCTURE USING TQC

Predicting changes in the business environment is difficult. Sales, production, and profits change in response to external influences such as an oil crisis, a low-growth economy, worldwide recession, foreign exchange rates, trade friction, import restrictions, and raw material costs, and these can sometimes threaten the existence of a company.

A lean and mean company organizational structure is important if it is to survive such severe changes in its business environment. What does strengthening organizational structure mean? We can look at each of the words in the phrase. ''Structure'' means both the physical and mental characteristics and the structural properties of a body. The word "strengthen" means to make tougher.

The organizational structure of a company is its power. It is the characteristics and the capabilities of the company, and more specifically, it is the ability to plan, to develop, to engineer, to sell, to compete on quality and cost, to control, to organize, and to solve problems. This can further be defined as the ability to process and arrange work, and the inherent engineering and control abilities derived from every employee's attitude toward the job and the capabilities he or she brings to the job. A company has the responsibility to maximize these abilities and to organize them.

The following procedures will help to strengthen the organizational structure of a company.

Procedures for Strengthening the Organizational Structure of a Company

1. *Identify the weaknesses in the company's structure.* Proper measures cannot be taken, no matter how much improving the company structure is talked about, if the weaknesses in the structure are not first exposed. The problems need to be made visible. Top management should initiate group discussions and clarify these weaknesses using an affinity chart or a characteristic/factor chart.

   Some examples of weaknesses are listed in Table 1.2.

2. *Clarify the objectives and the contents of structural improvement.* Determine what kind of company structure is desired.

3. *Set priorities for promoting TQC activities.* The structure of a company cannot be changed easily. Improvements must be made one at a time so that changes in the development can be observed. TQC is an effective means to achieve this. Once it has been decided to introduce TQC, priorities need to be set to achieve the structural improvements, and they should be established in specific terms so that they can be achieved by the company as a whole using TQC concepts and QC methods.

THE CHALLENGE TO IMPROVE QUALITY AT THE JAPAN STEEL WORKS, LTD.

The Japan Steel Works, Ltd. was founded in 1908 to produce weapons in the city of Muroran Hokkaido and thus is a company with a long history. It now produces and sells large steel castings and a variety of industrial machines, as well as mill products. In other words, it is a general manufacturer of steel and machines.

During the prewar and post-World War II periods, the company grew

TABLE 1.2. Examples of weakness.

No.	*Weakness*
1	Tendency toward product-out attitude
2	Tendency to depend only on one's own judgment
3	Tendency not to see the overall picture
4	Tendency to oversimplify
5	Tendency to be complacent
6	Tendency to think of one's own department or section
7	Tendency not to utilize data and information
8	Tendency not to foster employees' ability or potential
9	Tendency to do only that which is assigned
10	Tendency not to look for the causes to problems
11	Tendency to avoid making waves
12	Tendency to push everything onto one's subordinates
13	Tendency to be passive
14	Tendency to move without a plan
15	Tendency to neglect quality
16	Tendency to emphasize results
17	Tendency to think negatively
18	Tendency to depend on KKD (*Keiken*—experience; *Kan*—hunch; *Dokyo*—gut feelings)
19	Tendency to start things without finishing them
20	Tendency to cover problems with band-aids
21	Tendency to be satisfied with the status quo
22	Tendency to depend on others and not be accountable for one's own actions
23	Tendency not to take on difficult challenges
24	Tendency to act without a strategy
25	Tendency to give up too soon

steadily. Then, with the oil crisis and the deteriorating business environment as a result of the yen growing stronger, the company suffered losses in the period from 1976 to 1979, and bankruptcy seemed imminent.

M. Tateno became president in July of 1979. In October of that year he publicly announced that he would introduce TQC because fundamental changes in the organizational structure of the company were necessary in order to see this crisis through. Mr. Tateno stated at that time:

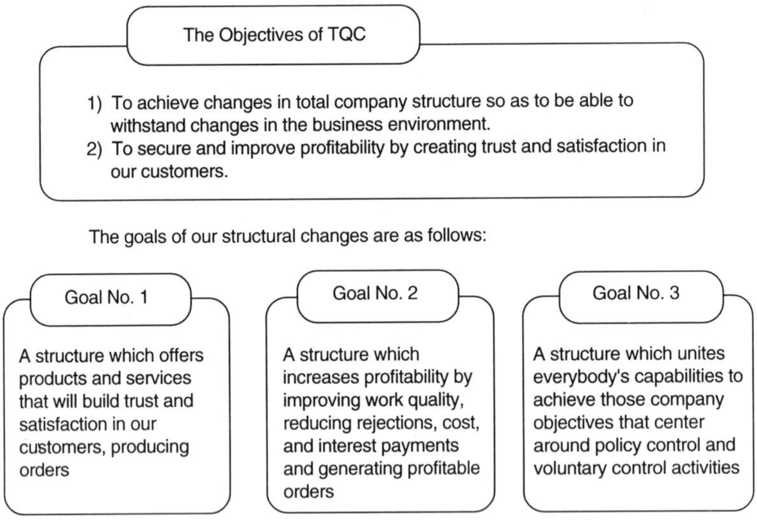

The Objectives of TQC

1) To achieve changes in total company structure so as to be able to withstand changes in the business environment.
2) To secure and improve profitability by creating trust and satisfaction in our customers.

The goals of our structural changes are as follows:

Goal No. 1

A structure which offers products and services that will build trust and satisfaction in our customers, producing orders

Goal No. 2

A structure which increases profitability by improving work quality, reducing rejections, cost, and interest payments and generating profitable orders

Goal No. 3

A structure which unites everybody's capabilities to achieve those company objectives that center around policy control and voluntary control activities

FIGURE 1.2.   Objectives of TQC at the Japan Steel Works.

I formally announce a companywide introduction of TQC. Our Hiroshima Works have received the Deming Prize as the result of a three-year effort [the divisional award, 1979]. The effects of this are being felt by all of us to some degree. Based on this experience, I believe that TQC is the proper means to achieve the structural improvements needed in a scientific, positive, and strong manner. This is necessary for Japan Steel Works to face the changes in our business environment.

Our objective is not just to win the Deming Prize but to produce high-quality products as inexpensively as possible through a coordinated total companywide establishment of rationalized production and control systems. We can predict from our experiences at the Hiroshima Works that the hardships required of our managers will be considerable. But I believe that specific steps must be undertaken immediately if we wish to look forward to the next one hundred years of this company's future.

Figure 1.2 shows the plan of action prepared at the time of the introduction of TQC to the entire company by all departments at Japan Steel Works.

Figure 1.3 shows the history of TQC promotion from 1979 through 1983 and the results that were recognized by the Deming Prize in 1983.

In October of 1983, President Tateno stated:

We have learned TQC in the past four years. Of course, we don't think that it is fully disseminated throughout the company yet, and we must keep on learning. But we have begun to feel that the changes we have made allow us to cope with the harsh business environment by rooting out deep weaknesses retained from our past. Our company, thanks to everyone's efforts, has

History of TQC promotion at the Japan Steel Works.

Item	1979	1980	1981	1982	1983
Objective		Penetration of TQC concept throughout company	Thorough implementation of policy control	Establishment of cross-functional management system	Enhancement of priority functions
Preparation of promo. group	• Established TQC promotion dept. (Hiroshima)(Jan. 1976)	• Established TQC promotion dept. (companywide) (Jan. 1980) • Established PLP in charge (Oct. 1980) (Muroran) (Yokohama) (Tokyo) (Engineering) • Established TQC promotion dept. (Jan.-Feb. 1980) • Established TQC promotion conference (Nov. 1980) (total company)			• Established QC functional committees (total co. Dec. 1982) • Established profit control committee (total co. Dec. 1983) • Established order intake control committee (total co. Feb. 1983)
Education	Attend QC seminars, study meetings of JUSE • QC seminars, QC circle seminars, test plan method seminars, reliability seminars, etc., PL seminars, PS study meets., 7 New Tools study meets., multivariate analysis study meets., etc.	Run guidance meets. with invited instructors / Multivariate analysis, quality function deployment, dispersion analysis, reliability, etc. / In-house QC method seminars, case study presentations, etc. / 7 Tools QC test plan method, 7 New QC Tools, reliability, multivariate analysis, etc.			
Voluntary control	Zero defect movement / Implemented policy control (Hiroshima)	Activation of voluntary control actions (dissemination of QC methods, awareness of improvement, etc.) / Implemented policy control (total company) (policy sheet, action plan sheet, control item list)			
Policy control	Policy control implementation (Hiroshima)		Policy control implementation manual (12/81), Policy deployment regulation (1/82), Policy deployment manual (12/82) / Implementation of AGS activities / AGS action implementation manual (Apr. 1983) / Deployment of policy per prod. (total co.) / Deployment of cross-functional policy (total company) / Medium term policy per product / med. term QA policy - med. term profit control policy - medium term order intake control policy		
QA	QA action implementation (Hiroshima) / Quality function deployment (QA chart, quality sheet, control process chart) / R & D system arrangement		QA system arrangement (total company) / Quality forecast control chart - QA action list - QA regulation (10/82) - Claim control regulation (3/82) / Enhancement of QA activities (total company) / PLP system arrangement / PLP manual (May 1981) / Enhancement of PLP activities / PL claim handling manual (Nov. 1982) / Enhancement of R&D control activities / Product development manual revision (1/82) - R&D regulation revision (7/82)		
Profit control			NE solution action implementation / NE solution action manual (Apr. 1983) / Profit control system arrangement / Profit control action list - regulation (Mar. 1983) / Enhancement of profit control activities		
Order intake control			SBU action implementation / SBU action manual (Apr. 1983) / Order intake control system arrangement / Order intake control manual (Oct. 1980) / Enhancement of order intake control activities / Order intake cont. reg. (11/82) Ord. intake cont. act. list (3/83)		
TQC introduction	TQC introduction/promotion (Hiroshima) / TQC introduction and promotion (Oct. 1979)	• Proclamation of companywide TQC introduction (Dec. 1978)			
Diagnosis	QC diagnosis (Hiroshima) (Dec. 1978) / • Deming Award Divisional (Hiroshima) (Nov. 1979)		President's audit implementation	QC audit (total company) / • (Muroran) (HQ) (Yokohama) (Engineering) (Tokyo) (Dec. 1981 - May 1982) / General evaluation meeting implementation	Enhancement of pres.'s audit (adopt common audit method) / Policy control - QA - Profit control - Order intake control
Effects		Clearer policy at job levels / Concept of market-in	Policy control system / More use of statistical method	Better cooperation among depts. / More active AGS actions	
Problems	Unclear policy / Weak market-in concept	Plan for policy control not specific / Weak companywide cooperation	Lack of upstream control, many rejects / Lack of profit and order intake controls	Lack of actions and evaluation for cross-functional management	

AGS: ambitious goal setting; SBU: strategic business unit

FIGURE 1.3. History of TQC promotion at the Japan Steel Works.

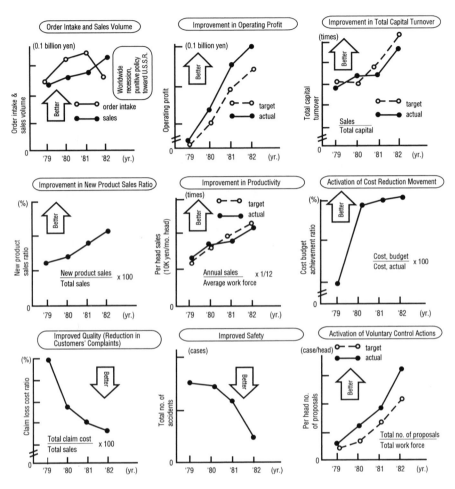

FIGURE 1.4.   Tangible effects of TQC.

recovered enough to be able to pay dividends for the first time since 1981, and at the same time to reduce the large debt from the past.

And, he added, "Had it not been for the revolution brought about by TQC, we would not be here today." The company has attained tangible and intangible benefits, as shown in Figure 1.4 and in Table 1.3.

For companies to improve and to stabilize their performance, and to expand in uncertain economic environments and face industrial competition, more timely responses to external changes and enhanced corporate structure are necessary. One must be careful to avoid the attitude that merely by introducing TQC company structure can be improved. But TQC can be effective in building a tough and resilient company structure, as shown by the example of Japan Steel Works.

TABLE 1.3.   Intangible effects of TQC.

Aim	*Intangible effects*
Improvement and maintenance of quality of products and services	• Establishment of market-input-based awareness • More recognition of responsibility of each department and importance of improvement process • Re-recognition of importance of education, more seminars
Improvement of quality of work	• Proper collection of data and better analysis for policy determination • Establishment of concept of dispersion in data • Establishment of recognition of "Control = PDCA cycles" in form of action
Consolidation of total capability	• Activation of AGS (ambitious goal seeking) for more challenging attitude by all • Better matching of activities of top and bottom through diagnostics • Realization of interdepartmental competition and cooperation and activation of SBU (strategic business unit) system • Activation of voluntary control • Heightened morale of all for more positive attitude

2

Management with Participation by Everyone

—Unite employees' capabilities companywide to achieve the best outcome.

TQC AND EMPLOYEE GROUPS

As is evident in the definition of TQC given earlier, participation, action, and execution of wisdom by all departments within an organization and everyone in the company are necessary to promote QC effectively. That is, QC cannot succeed unless "management with participation by everyone = TQC" becomes a reality.

E. Imura, former president (currently an adviser) of Tokai Rika Co., which manufactures automotive components such as switches and locks, said,

> One, taking action with the participation of everyone and, two, implementation of QC throughout all company functions are necessary to overcome structural weaknesses and adverse effects of high growth rates, as well as to improve a company. I have reached the conclusion that only TQC can help to make the above happen and have decided to introduce TQC into our company beginning in 1974.[4a]

This statement is based on a strong belief that TQC is "the best scientific concept/tool that is common to the entire company and all its employees" to form employee groups for positive activities with a rational foundation. At his company, the quality of the company is viewed from two perspectives, i.e., company "performance" and company "character." A company consists of people with emotions and intelligence. The formation of a group of people full of vitality and positive interpersonal relationships against a

14

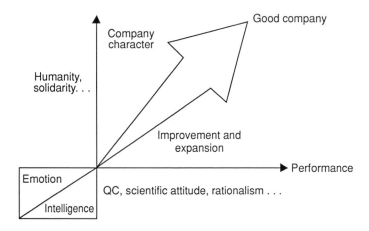

FIGURE 2.1.   Company character and performance.

background of both strict science and humanity, where passion and intellect can ignite creativity to the maximum, is the ideal (see Figure 2.1).

This company is promoting management improvement centered around TQC, on the basis of a belief that company character and performance can grow interdependently and synergistically. The TQC program of Tokai Rika was awarded the Deming Prize in 1978.

STRATEGIES TO DEVELOP PARTICIPATION BY EVERYONE

All a business enterprise's activities are performed by people. Although computerization and robotics are very much with us, it is people who handle them. It is not an overstatement to say that the future of a company is secure only when the ability of everyone within the company is used to its fullest through management of participation by everyone. "Participation by everyone" means that QC is implemented:

- with participation by everyone
- throughout all departments—planning, design, engineering, production, purchasing, marketing, general administration, etc.
- with involvement of top management, department heads, section heads, group heads, managers, foremen, staff, and workers (which is easier said than done)

Various types of interference can occur with participation by everyone. What are the obstacles that can interfere with participation by everyone and how can they be overcome?

When Top Management Does Not Take Leadership

Two examples of this problem follow.

1. Top management does not know about QC with participation by everyone or is not interested.
2. Top management talks about QC with participation by everyone but does nothing.

Prof. T. Ikezawa of Waseda University says in his book, *Do's and Don'ts of QC* (JUSE Press), "Do not introduce TQC unless the president (or the No. 2 person in charge) is serious about it—the No. 3 person in charge won't do!" TQC goes nowhere unless the top takes leadership. Some even say that the T in TQC stands for top. If the "top" is not interested and does not take leadership, he or she must be pushed towards the idea and have the benefits of TQC explained convincingly. This advocacy role is played by a director in charge of TQC or by a TQC promoter.

Several methods for pushing the top person are:

- Have the person attend QC seminars (for example, Special Top Managers' Course or Senior Managers' Course, which are held by JUSE).
- Have him attend QC conferences (e.g., Top Management Conference, Department Section Heads and Staffs Conference, or QC Circle Conference, such as those held by JUSE).
- Ask the head of a related company or customer or supplier to talk with him.
- Introduce QC circles or hold in-house meetings to demonstrate the benefits of QC.
- Implement QC in a model business department or model plant and show him the results.
- Ask QC professionals for a QC diagnosis with him present.

At any rate, start by giving him some stimulus, something to get excited over, although the tactics will be different for different individuals.

When There Are Objecting Senior Managers or Department Heads

It is inevitable that some senior managers or department heads will object to TQC. They will say, "Such a thing will reduce order taking," or, "What good is it? It will only create complications." These are the people who have expanded sales and contributed to new product development without TQC. Yet times change and conventional means seldom work after a while. But the rate of increase in sales and profit may well be decreasing without these objecting people realizing it. The first thing to do is to have these people learn about QC. They can attend special senior management courses or department/section head courses for QC study. At the same time they can be told what other managers are trying to do and with what kind of problem awareness. A ''QC diagnosis'' can be performed using facts and data to help them recognize the weaknesses in the present situation.

When TQC Promotion Is Not Adequate

Often entities called ''TQC promotion room'' or ''TQC committee'' are established to be in charge of TQC promotion. In general, these sections are in charge of jobs such as:

- Research, study, and development of QC
- Planning and organization of TQC
- Education and total company dissemination of QC
- Audit of, and guidance for, TQC implementation

The role of a TQC promoter is important. The characteristics required of someone in charge of TQC promotion are:

- Good human relations skills and the ability to win over others
- Able to plan with flexibility
- The will to achieve things with self-motivation
- Impassioned
- Have shop floor experience and be versed in the specific technology
- Healthy and able to take stress
- Understand QC

People with these qualifications are hard to come by, especially because people who are already central figures in departments are busy. However, it is important to pick the best ones as promoters to devote their time to the project, because the desire of top management for TQC promotion will be exemplified by the assignment of such good people. Particularly, for the initial TQC promotion, people with the will to fight and achieve should be picked, even if their QC knowledge is not complete. The knowledge can be acquired later.

When Corporate and Sales Departments
Do Not Follow the Promotion

Often the line functions can get serious about TQC but the corporate office and sales departments are cool about it. Everyone's participation is needed to promote TQC.

QA and new-product development cannot be performed without corporate functions where long-term planning, policy control, product planning, and human resource development are handled. The production department loses work if products cannot be sold. Especially in times of fierce sales competition, the sales department has to participate in TQC. Departments that are not positive about participation should be scrutinized for the manner in which work is done, and any problems discovered should be improved in a QC way for better control, rather than just ramming TQC down peoples' throats. In this way, these departments will learn methods of improvement and control that will give them a better taste for QC.

Summary

There are many problems in promoting TQC. This is only natural because the dust collected over a long time needs to be wiped off. However, unless the objecting forces can be turned around to your side, participation by all cannot be realized. There are many serious promoters of TQC among senior managers and department heads who were once in the anti-QC camp.

PROMOTING TQC WITH PARTICIPATION BY EVERYONE

The following four steps are important ones to be taken here for TQC promotion with participation by everyone.

Step 1. *Top management announces the introduction of TQC.* Demonstrate top management's attitude toward, decision for, and commitment to TQC by announcing clear TQC objectives for "the betterment of the company."

Step 2. *Start introducing TQC.* Clearly present management policy and action guidelines for all, and start TQC activities. QC education is important for correct understanding of QC, so make an educational plan and implement it without fail.

Step 3. *Perform a general check-up.* Problems must be made visible to improve the quality of the work. A "general check-up" means checking all work by everyone to discover problems, and pinpointing items to be improved. Everyone is to go through an awareness revolution and to search positively for problems that

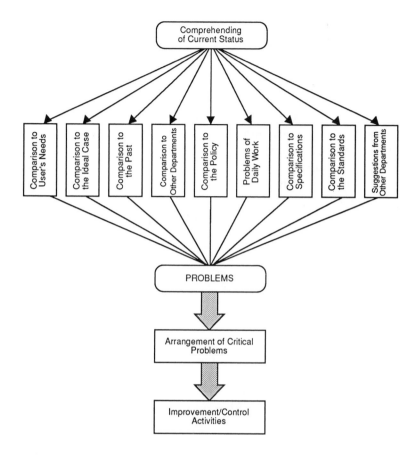

FIGURE 2.2. General check-up for improvement and control activities.

should be correlated with those of other departments in order to solve them. (See Figure 2.2)

Of course, not just problems related to daily management but also those of policy control and performance of established policy need to be checked out.

Step 4. *Deploy improvement activities with participation by everyone.* Promote improvement activities for problems and tasks of management, and structure improvements for those problems discovered by the overall check-up, using participation by everyone.

Modes of improvement actions can be:

- addressing problems on the job through supervisors
- addressing problems with the QC team or project team
- addressing problems with the QC circle

The most appropriate mode to select depends on the magnitude of the problem, the degree of difficulty, and the scope of involvement of other departments.

CONSCIOUSNESS RAISING AND UNITING EFFORTS AT KAJIMA CORPORATION

Kajima Corporation is a major company with 38.3 billion yen in capital (1984), 11 branch offices throughout Japan, and approximately 16,000 employees. It handles more than 2,000 construction projects at any one time. Since its founding in 1849, it has expanded steadily as a general contractor for construction and land development. However, it was faced with a series of new difficulties as a result of the oil crises and changes in its business environment. R. Ishikawa (now the company's chairman) decided to introduce TQC when he became president in February 1978 and talked about the objectives and necessity of doing so in his first speech. A summary of the speech is given below.

*   *   *

TQC Introduction and Its Objectives

First of all, what I wish to ask of you as the president of this company is a moral build-up of and by each one of you and the uniting of all individual capabilities based on such a build-up.

The whole world is faced with new trials and there are many difficult problems, both internationally and domestically; however, a company must face these difficulties, as an important part of our nation and society, with a sincere feeling for our responsibility towards society, while establishing a base for its own improvement and renewal so as to find the road to new harmony and development.

This company has achieved tremendous growth during the period of strong economic growth and has built a foundation for present stability. But new times require us to act with a new awareness and new capabilities, while depending upon the principles and the rules accumulated in the past. We must break away from old bad habits and must endeavor to build an open company where there are no dark corners or forgotten sectors.

Improvement of quality throughout all facets of management is very much necessary to realize our company's new forward motion. Quality here is not opposed to volume, but has a positive nature that supports volume and creates new volume.

I wish to propose the introduction of TQC, which is the best modern management control tool to further our company's structural improvement toward the above-stated objectives.

Complacency, arrogance, easygoingness—i.e., bad habits and aftereffects of the high-growth period—have resulted in decreases in market share and profitability as companies now enter the low-growth period.[1b]

*   *   *

President Ishikawa decided upon introducing TQC from the viewpoint that structural improvements must be addressed with a renewal of spirit, and (as we have seen) he called for a "morale build-up and uniting of all individual capabilities." The company has aimed at:

- Morale build-up (renewal of awareness)
- Establishing scientific control
- Enhancing business competitiveness based on the above with a basic policy for "building a healthy company structure which assures continued success" through morale build-up, heightened loyalty to the company, and a uniting of all capabilities. The company's TQC promotion with participation by all is summarized in Table 2.1.

As a result, the company had 1.7 times the order backlog on construction volume and 1.6 times the sales revenue and operational profits in 1982 as compared to the pre-TQC introduction levels (1977), along with various other

TABLE 2.1.   History of TQC promotion at Kajima Corp.

Period	*1978*	*1979–80*	*1981–*
Theme of each period	In search of new control system	Toward quality improvement	Long-term management plan with emphasis on quality
Priority actions in each period	• Dissemination of TQC concept • Preparation of basis for TQC promotion	• Morale build-up and study of QC methods with TQC education & QC group activities • Enhancement of QC and QC-like improvement of daily work • Enhancement of departmental control centered around policy control	• TQC deployment toward objectives • Improvement/ strengthening of QA system • Preparation of overall control system for execution of total control

benefits such as quality improvement, productivity improvement, safety improvement, and cost reduction. Further, these intangible effects from participation by all were realized:

- The desire to listen to others, including the voices of those from downstream processes, was established for better in-house communication.
- Morale was raised because the voices from the shop floor began to be reflected in clearer policy formation, and more honest opinions began to surface.
- The awareness of one's responsibility and role became stronger, and more serious attention began to be paid to real problems.
- Hidden human resources were discovered during the action process with participation by all, and the basis for human resource build-up was created.

3

Quality First

—Guarantee profit by making quality a priority.

SEEKING PROFIT BY MAKING QUALITY A PRIORITY

Securing profits is necessary to the success of any enterprise, yet it must be based on making quality a priority.

In the short run, cheap products will sell even if their quality is poor and expensive products will sell as long as the quality is good, but for products to keep on selling, quality must be there at the proper price.

A special issue of the U.S. magazine *Business Week* on the theme "American Managers Strive for Quality—Japanese Style" talks about the efforts of the Japanese towards quality as one of the differences between the United States and Japan in the area of QC.[5] This issue is based on a paper by Dr. Juran, which was presented at ICQC 1978 in Tokyo and is annotated with comments from industry executives.

The contents compare the attitudes of U.S. and Japanese industries towards product quality and urge U.S. industry, which was once the teacher of the Japanese, to improve. The issue caused a bit of a sensation among Japanese manufacturers as well. It compares QC approaches and specific practices in Japan and the United States and includes comments from representative people in various fields. The main topics are:

- *Management policy*—In the U.S., short-term planning is common; it is mainly based on fire-fighting. In Japan, long-term planning is done to prevent failures.

- *Background of business management*—In Japan, management planning centers around quality, whereas in the U.S., marketing and financial aspects are at the core.

- *Attitude of investors and shareholders*—In the U.S., short-term (quarterly) profit improvement/maintenance is of prime interest, interfering with long-term plans for quality improvement. In Japan, more stable and steadier growth is sought rather than short-term profit.

- *Employee education*—In the U.S., investment in employee education is suspect, while in Japan the importance of educating people to build good quality is well recognized and practiced.

- *Attitude towards defects*—In the U.S., defects, to a certain degree, are expected, whereas in Japan, defects are looked upon as shameful and reduction of defects is sought, as well as reduction in the number of components through improvement of function.

- *Selection of vendors*—In the U.S., human error after the contract has been signed is seen as inevitable so a certain acceptable quality level (AQL) is established. In Japan, vendors who can ship perfect products are nurtured by always checking first whether or not vendors have production processes that can provide good quality.

This is the gist of the special *Business Week* issue.

Since then, the number of U.S. companies introducing and promoting Japanese-style TQC has increased. Companies such as Ford, Hewlett-Packard, and Xerox, where there is a high potential for QC, are deploying it.

WHAT DOES "QUALITY FIRST" MEAN?

"Quality First" is the concept of putting quality ahead of sales increases, cost reduction, and efficiency improvement, and placing a priority on quality improvement.

This is easier said than done. Many companies talk about Quality First in their company policy but their effort for quality, when compared to that for sales increases and profit maintenance, is doubtful. Some companies do not care about product quality and design quality, or they pay attention to QA while talking about Quality First, but are serious only about order taking and cost reductions.

Sooner or later these companies are hit by major market complaints, give a lot of grief to their customers, waste a lot of money on repairs, and lose valuable customers. Often, these companies do not realize that the major loss is due to failures. As shown in Figure 3.1, total loss related to quality is not negligible. When this total loss exceeds 2 percent of total sales the situation is critical.

There are still some people who say that improvement in quality leads to cost increases, which reduce profit in turn. However, this is a big mistake. Real quality sells, it helps reduce rejects and failures, it cuts down repairs and scrap, it boosts trust from customers, and it results in sales increases and large cost reductions. The source of profit maintenance can indeed be said to be "Quality First."

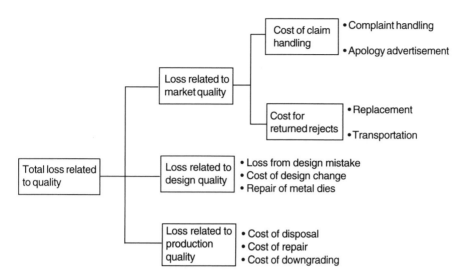

FIGURE 3.1. Losses related to quality problems.

The term "quality" needs to be explained a little here. In the past, "quality" was considered to be "the degree of compliance with specifications." However, consumer-oriented quality started to be required because of recent slack in demand, diversification of market requirements, and intensified market competition. That is, it became necessary to:

- Investigate and understand "market quality"; i.e., latent demand and apparent demand of the market.
- Establish "design quality" (quality demanded by consumers that is converted to quality characteristics and formed into product specifications; also called "target quality").
- Realize "compliance quality" in the production stage (actual quality of a product aimed at design quality is called "compliance quality"; also called "accomplished quality" or "matched quality").
- Provide not only "so-so quality" (products of normal function without failures or rejects) but also "attractive quality" (products of creativeness and of assured quality that are bought with excitement).

The following actions must be performed to realize "Quality First."

10 Means to Achieve "Quality First"

1. Investigate the market: collect and analyze information as to the desires of consumers and the salable level of quality.
2. Plan market-creating products that create new demand by answering users' needs.

3. Develop products that achieve design targets after deciding on a target quality based on an analysis of demand.

4. Design production processes by deciding on standards for the building-in of planned and designed quality during the production process.

5. Perform trouble-forecasting for each stage of planning, design, and prototype production to prevent similar troubles in later processes.

6. Perform process control by maintaining process capabilities for critical quality characteristics.

7. Inspect to avoid the flow of poor-quality product lots to later processes by evaluating quality.

8. Handle complaints quickly and appropriately by enhancing the service system.

9. Enhance the QA system by going back to the earliest stages to locate the causes of troubles.

10. Go after the real causes of quality problems by using QC methods effectively, trying to solve problems, and enhancing standards as a back-up.

MANAGEMENT BY QUALITY FIRST IN THE AISIN GROUP

Many companies are proclaiming "Quality First" as their management philosophy:

- "Quality is Supremacy"—Aisin Seiki.
- "Give back to society with Quality First"—Kyosan Denki.
- "Contribute to society with the creation of affluence through better quality"—Shimizu Corporation.
- "Produce and market superior products"—Kobayashi-Kosei.

The Aisin Group is one of the companies that achieved growth and expansion as a manufacturer of automotive parts and chemical products on the coattails of the expansion of the motor vehicle market. As shown in Table 3.1, the group consists of a total of seven companies—six manufacturers of various products centered around Aisin Seiki and one sales company.

This group is planning to deploy a strong improvement in company structure and to strengthen its actual performance by coping with diversifying and sophisticated demands for quality as well as by intensifying its sales efforts. To beat the competition, they are introducing TQC in a positive manner under their "quality supremacy" management philosophy (see Figure

TABLE 3.1. Companies of Aisin Group as of 1984.

Name of Company	Employees	Business	Year of Deming Prize	Year of Nippon QC Award
Aisin Seiki Co., Ltd.	8,200	Automotive parts, home appliance production	1972	1977
Takaoka Industries	2,000	Automotive cast parts	1980	
Aisin Chemical Co., Ltd.	550	Chemical products	1982	
Aisin Warner, Ltd.	2,350	Automotive, automatic transmission parts	1977	1982
Aisin Sales Co.	42	Home appliance sales		
Aisin Light Metals Co.	700	Aluminum die-cast products	1983	
Shinwa Industries, Ltd.	650	Automotive parts	1982	
Group Total	14,492			

3.2).[1b] M. Toyoda, chairman of Aisin Group, discusses, below, his "Quality company management for quality supremacy and its implementation."

*   *   *

Aisin-Seiki and Aisin-Warner have gone through many difficulties under the changing business environment during my life as a manager. Each time, I have emphasized a timely policy such as enhancement of scientific control systems, QA, new-product development, and safe environment, to overcome these difficulties. The basis of these policies has always been "Quality Supremacy." This is my basic concept of management.

I have continuously sought for the key that promises continued success as an enterprise against the background of such factors as auto safety, exhaust fumes, and energy conservation.

Every time I go abroad I have looked for the answer to the question, "Why do Japanese cars sell well?" All the dealers I posed the question to said that it was Japanese quality that sells. The president of Volvo, with which we do business, said, "Because we get parts from all over the world and assemble them into our cars, poor quality will not do, even at less cost.

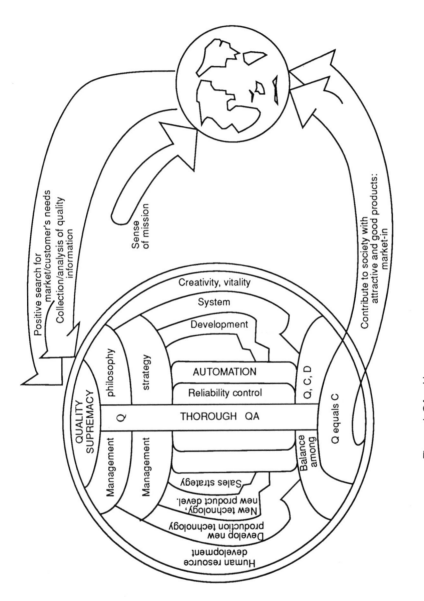

Thorough QA achieves:
- Customer satisfaction
- People's happiness
- Prosperity of company

FIGURE 3.2. Management philosophy of Aisin Warner, Ltd.

Therefore, we go for supreme quality." This is absolutely right, and we believe that the key to a company's survival is a level of quality acceptable to society.

From the beginning I believed that Quality First is the least wasteful method because good cost and delivery come out of the search for quality.

With this concept of quality supremacy I am chasing after the dream of an enterprise that contributes to society and human prosperity. I am trying to raise the level of engineering effort and control, always aiming at the following two points: (1) search for market needs in a positive manner and develop new technology to create new demand; and (2) try to improve the control level further and challenge management efficiency and problem awareness to the ultimate.

I believe that such technology and control are the prime motivating forces for future development of an enterprise.

Since the establishment of Aisin, much improvement has been made in engineering, as in the promotion of R&D with industry/academic cooperation through deployment of an enhanced engineering development system. But when I looked at the control phase, it was a little behind engineering, so I felt the need to raise this level. I believe that the control phase must progress along with changes in engineering and the business environment, as engineering progresses at a rapid pace. Healthy management is possible only when engineering and control are smoothly meshing together.

Based on the above observation, I think management needs to improve the company structure with a new vision every five years. Is this not why we utilize the Deming Prize or the Japan QC Award as means for achieving a vision, and come up with timely themes every five years as targets and adjust our method of control accordingly?

Acting on the belief that this is the only right thing to do if our enterprise is to continue its existence, I manage our company with a vision for every five years. I firmly believe that TQC is the most appropriate method to bond all of the company together in the QC way of thinking. Based on this way of thinking, I have made efforts so that various functions that produce product quality and other quality can be controlled sufficiently.

I term such management "quality management" and call the company with this good QC way of management a Quality Company.[4b]

*   *   *

Figure 3.3 shows the history of TQC promotion at Aisin Light Metals as an example of TQC promotion in the Aisin Group.[1a] This company is a manufacturer specializing in die-cast aluminum products, primarily for the automotive industry. It has 700 employees and 14.8 billion yen in sales (as of 1983) and was awarded the Deming Prize for a medium- to small-sized company in 1983.

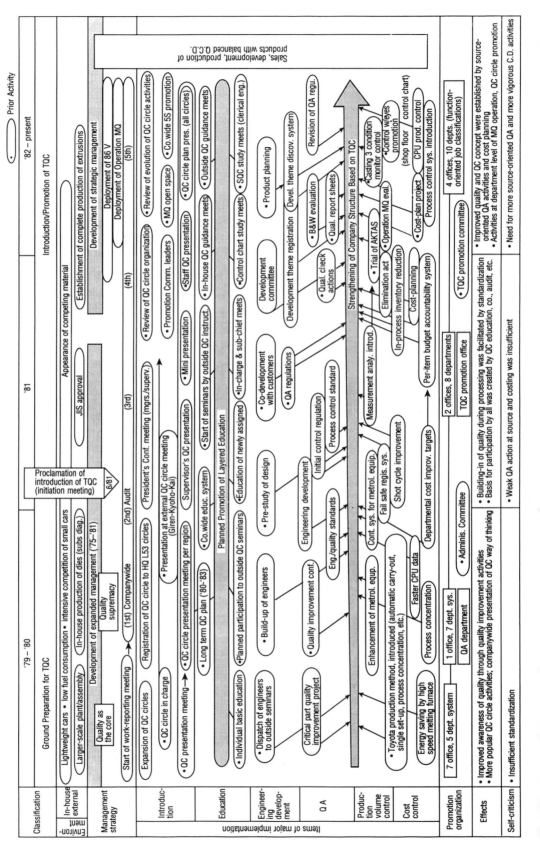

4

The PDCA Cycle

—Run through the control cycle thoroughly.

WHAT IS CONTROL?

The term "control" is popular these days. Quality control, cost control, production control, safety control, sales control, personnel control, out-sourcing control—the list is endless. According to the *Kojien Dictionary*, published by Iwanami Shoten, Publishers, "Control means to assert jurisdiction and then exercise it," but generally it means "to set a good goal and achieve it."

The root of the Japanese word for control, *kanri*, has two parts:

1. *KAN*—This character consists of the smaller characters (radicals) for "bamboo" and "administer," thus, "the existence of knots here and there within a certain action."

2. *RI*—This character consists of the smaller characters for "king" and "native place"; the character for "native place" can be broken down further to the radicals "soil" and "rice farm." Thus, one's native place touches the elements and provides sustenance. And we always see a straight road between the rice fields and houses, symbolizing the steady, direct way. The character for "king" contains the character for the numeral 3 and a vertical line, so 3 means multiplicity and the vertical line connects these multiple things. Therefore, the word *ri* shows "the route (logic) through various subjects and factors."

From this etymology the word *kanri* can be understood as "to perform things, go stage by stage (knot by knot) and follow logic, with consideration for various factors along the way."

Whenever *kanri* (control) is mentioned one thinks of enforcement or re-

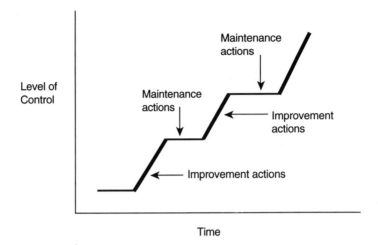

FIGURE 4.1. Control activities for quality maintenance and improvement.

striction, but that is not what it means. Dr. Juran said, "Control is the whole body of actions to decide on a plan (standard) and achieve it."

From the above explanation, "control" can be defined as "all activities necessary to achieve a certain objective, rationally and effectively, which are based on the running of the PDCA cycle (see next section)."

This set of control activities (broader meaning) has two parts (see Figure 4.1). The first is the "action of maintenance," which checks whether work is performed according to standard to produce the desired results and, if not, to take necessary action.

The second part is the "action of improvement," which sets the targets, such as quality improvement and cost reduction at higher than present levels, plans for their achievement, and acts accordingly.

WHAT IS THE PDCA CYCLE?

For both maintenance and improvement actions, it is important to repeat the PDCA cycle shown in Figure 4.2, i.e.,

$$\text{plan} \rightarrow \text{do} \rightarrow \text{check} \rightarrow \text{act}$$

Since running this cycle constitutes control, the PDCA cycle is also called a "control cycle" or "circle of control."

These four steps are further explained here.

PDCA Cycle

Step 1. *PLAN*—For making plans, it is important to:
1. clarify objectives and determine quality characteristics (control items)
2. set target values
3. determine the method of achievement of objectives

Step 2. *DO*—This step can be broken down into:
1. education and training in methods
2. implementation
3. collection of data on quality characteristics according to a set method

Step 3. *CHECK*—In this step, the status of the action and results is checked, evaluated, and confirmed:
1. Check if work was performed according to standards.
2. Check if various measurements and test results are in compliance with criteria.
3. Check if quality characteristics match the target values.

Step 4. *ACT*—Take action based on the results of Step 3:
1. If it is off the work standard, take corrective action to meet the standard.
2. If abnormal, find the cause and take actions to prevent repetition.
3. Improve job setup or sequence of work.

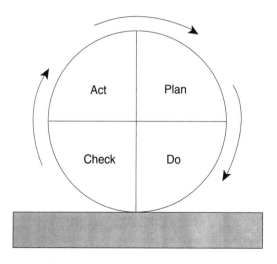

FIGURE 4.2.   The PDCA cycle.

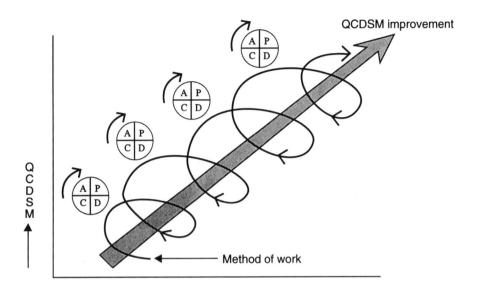

FIGURE 4.3. "Spiralling up" quality by applying PDCA.

Running the above steps in an exacting manner is important.

In the past, "plan-do-see" was popular, but "see" could be understood as just "look," which looks only at the result. This "see" is "check" and "act" in the field of QC.

People tend to stop at *DO* in the four steps of PDCA. "Doing" things with short-term vision cannot achieve good results. A thorough "plan," "check" of results, and "action" therefore are emphasized in QC.

Running a PDCA to go up to the next higher level of improvement based on self-reflection and action-taking is called "spiral-up" (see Figure 4.3).

PDCA IN PROCESS CONTROL

Thorough process control is necessary for production at a plant. The check-points for PDCA in process control are listed in Table 4.1. It is hoped that this list will be used for control activity on the shop floor or workplace by oneself or in a group.

PDCA FOR QUALITY MAINTENANCE
IN CONSTRUCTION WORK

K. Construction Co. has suffered a lot because of defective process control and repairs. PDCA was performed after TQC was introduced to establish thorough process control and assure passing on of good quality to later processes. This example is shown in Figure 4.4.

TABLE 4.1. PDCA check points for process control.

Steps	Check points
Plan	1. Are the true quality characteristics desired by customers understood?
	2. Is the relationship between quality and the 4Ms (machine, man, material, and method) classified?
	3. Is standards manual (work, engineering, and QC process standards, etc.) established?
	4. Are standards correctly understood?
	5. Are procedures for establishment, revision, and control of standards determined?
	6. Is work standard prepared with inputs of engineering, QA departments, and subordinates?
	7. Are adequate work know-how and cautions built into the work standard?
	8. Is handling of equipment, tools, and instruments specified?
	9. Is emergency procedure or place to report to specified?
	10. Are subject contents of work standard and their significance a part of education and training?
Do	1. Is work being done assuredly and as standardized?
	2. Are standardized material, machinery, tools, and instruments provided as specified?
	3. Is assignment of workers proper for their abilities and traits?
	4. Are lighting, ventilation, temperature, etc. adequate?
Check	1. Is work being done according to instructions?
	2. Is check being made by use of check sheet, control chart, etc.—i.e., the QC methods?
	3. Is check being made not only on the result but also on causes?
	4. Is supervisor visiting work area regularly?
Act	1. Are criteria for anomalies clear?
	2. Are reporting method, address, person in-charge, etc. established for engineering?
	3. Is process abnormality handled expeditiously?
	4. Is cause-finding for abnormality adequate?
	5. Is preventive measure taken?

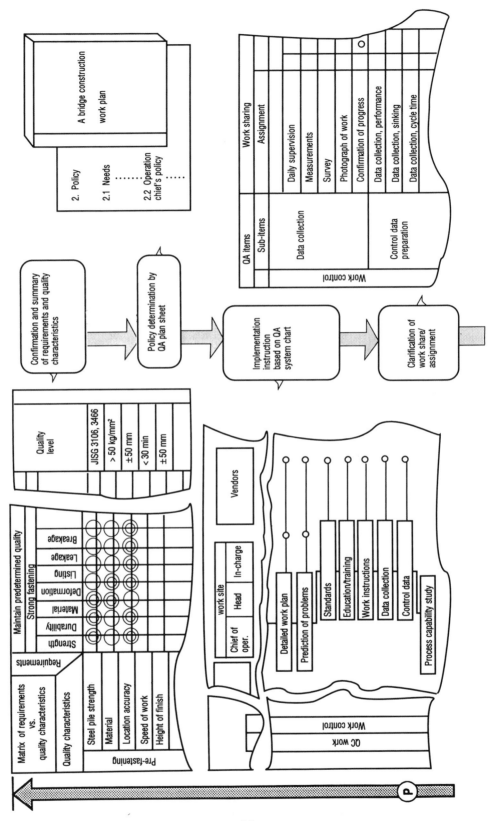

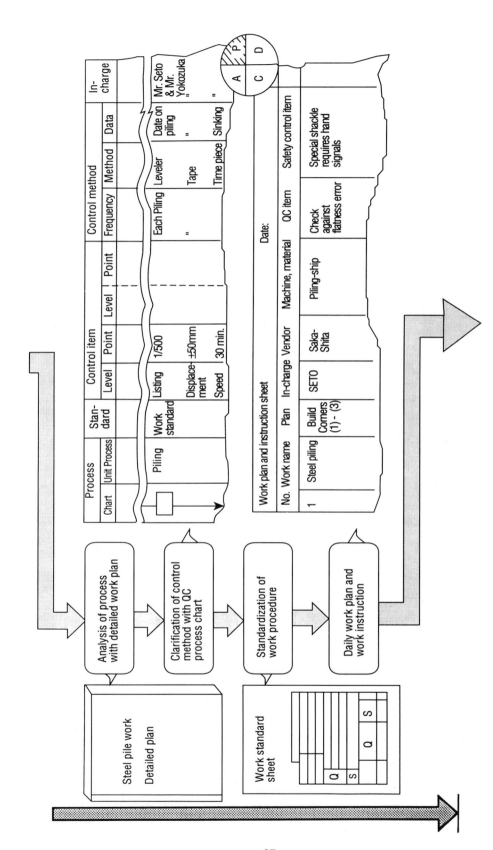

FIGURE 4.4. PDCA of process control for bridge construction (*continues on next page*).

37

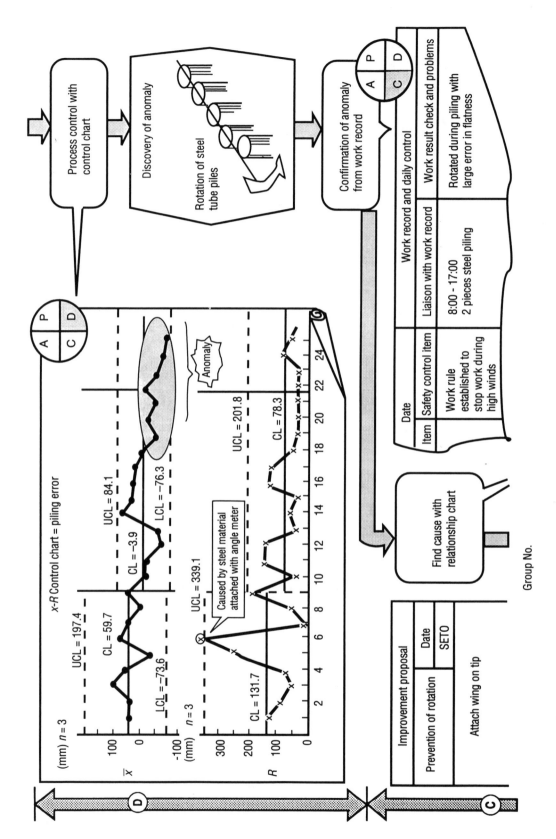

Process control with control chart

Discovery of anomaly

Rotation of steel tube piles

Confirmation of anomaly from work record

Find cause with relationship chart

A	P
C	D

x̄-R Control chart = piling error

(mm) *n* = 3

UCL = 197.4

CL = 59.7

UCL = 84.1

CL = -3.9

LCL = -76.3

LCL = -73.6

Anomaly

(mm) *n* = 3

UCL = 339.1

UCL = 201.8

CL = 78.3

CL = 131.7

Caused by steel material attached with angle meter

x̄

R

100
0
-100

300
200
100
0

2 4 6 8 10 12 14 16 18 20 22 24

	Work record and daily control		
Date			
Item	Safety control item	Liaison with work record	Work result check and problems
	Work rule established to stop work during high winds	8:00 - 17:00 2 pieces steel piling	Rotated during piling with large error in flatness

A	P
C	D

Improvement proposal		
	Date	
Prevention of rotation		SETO
Attach wing on tip		

Group No.

D

C

38

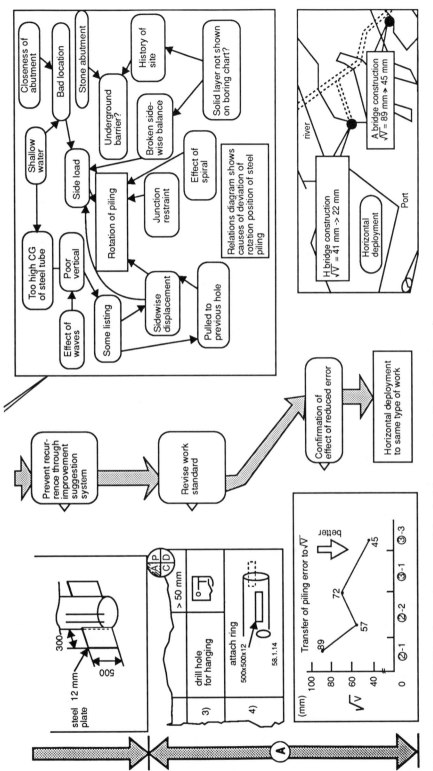

FIGURE 4.4. PDCA of process control for bridge construction (*continued*).

39

5

Focusing on Priorities

—Determine priority problems and attack them.

WHAT DOES IT MEAN TO FOCUS ON PRIORITIES?

There are many problems in the workplace. The reasons for variation in work results are numerous. It is important to select from among them those that need to be addressed first. However, not all factors can be treated, because of limited funds, time, and manpower and because it is not very efficient, either. Therefore, look for those factors that can have the greatest impact and tackle those. In other words, it is important to take care of the vital few rather than the trivial many.

"Focusing on priorities" means focusing on items that will yield major improvements. Note that there are only a few really important items among the many problems, and also that the same amount of effort for improvement results in a greater effect when applied to an important problem.

DEFINING PRIORITY ITEMS

Once the priorities have been chosen, the attack must be limited to the problems selected.

A problem can be defined as *the difference between the target to be achieved and the current conditions.* Among the problem items, the priority items are:

- Elements, tasks, and themes for achievement that have a great impact when dealt with successfully.

- Items of importance among higher ranking targets.

- Items that need to be improved or solved to strengthen the company structure.

- Obstacles to achieving management goals.

- Items that must be improved and solved to reach a target.

Understand the real conditions:

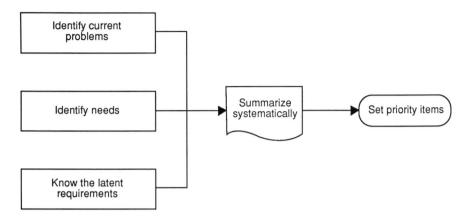

FIGURE 5.1.   Procedure for determining priority items.

The following effects can be expected when the above priority items are addressed:

- Clarification of the real priorities for management targets can promote steady and efficient achievement of goals.

- A QC answer to solving priority problems results in efficient problem solution and improved work methods.

- Solving priority items with cooperation among corporate departments, business units, and plants builds an interdepartmental unity.

DETERMINING PRIORITY ITEMS

Priority orientation is important for efficient promotion of company structural improvements based on long-term goals and for improvement of quality and profit.

Priority items must be determined for this orientation. Then all employees can combine their capabilities, use QC methods positively, and promote problem solution effectively. The method of setting priority items is explained below (see Figure 5.1).

Procedure for Determining Priority Items

Step 1. *List present problems.* Compare the present products of your own company with those of competitors and analyze performance, price, etc. to clarify problems to be solved and tasks to be performed. As for policy control, clarify problem points by checking the progress status of the prior period's tasks, and reflect on them. An overall check of, and reflection on, the work methods, set-ups, and processes are important, too.

Step 2. *Study wishes and instructions from management.* The desired items of top management and department heads and the instructions of these people are to be clarified at the same time. The needs of the market, of users, and of partner companies are to be understood.

Step 3. *List latent requirements.* Collect data on the strength of other companies or other departments: new products, new technology, new methods, market share, sales, etc. Then forecast a change in needs, trends, and future conditions to visualize the seeds that can create new demand.

Step 4. *Systematically summarize problems and requirements.* Summarize the problems and requirements listed in Steps 1 through 3, using required-quality deployment charts, system charts, etc.

Step 5. *Set priorities.* Rate the summarized problems and requirements for criticality, giving due weight to requirements, effects, feasibility, and difficulty when choosing priority items. A matrix chart can be of help here.

For priority items, essential conditions and development targets are to be assigned. ''Development target'' means (1) the aim, (2) the target value, (3) the condition to be achieved, and (4) time to achieve it. The points for determining priority items are:

Determining Priority Items
- Look for large contributions to performance (sales, profit, etc.).
- Look for maximum room for improvement.
- Look for big differences between present and target conditions.
- Look for a wide range of application for quantity, product areas, and departments.
- Look for challenging breakthroughs.
- Look for problematical trends.
- Look for future improvements of company structure.
- Look for solvable problems demanding a reasonable amount of effort in terms of work, time, and investment.
- Look for those items related to top management policy.
- Look for improvements that are desired by and of interest to top management.

CREATING SPECTACULAR PRODUCTS
BY FOCUSING ON PRIORITIES—
EXAMPLE: COMPACT CAMERA

In this age of shorter product life cycles and diversified demands, there are some hit products. Recent examples are:

- Ultra-thin, ultra-compact desk calculator computer [SL-800] with a 0.8cm thickness, 5cm × 7cm size (Casio Computer Co., Ltd.).

- Auto-zooming copier machine [EP 450 Z] with stepless zoom and reduction and automatic paper size selector that detects the size of originals (Minolta Co.).

- Refrigerator deodorizer "Odor Watch-Dog" with easy-to-see effectiveness gauge and when-to-replace indicator (Sekisui Chemical Co., Ltd.).

- W & D (wet and dry) electric shaver that can be used with soap and water [ES-862] (Matsushita Electric Works, Ltd.).

These products are the results of a timely response to the market's needs based on verification of concepts and clear priority setting.

The compact camera Konica C-35 EF of Konishiroku Photo Industry Co., Ltd. is an example of priority setting for new product development, although it is not really that new.[6] This company planned the development of a camera that provides family photographers with a little easier and more consistent quality of picture-taking.

The result of its investigation into consumer camera-use indicated that:

- Electronic shutters were being used, longer time exposures were possible, and proper exposure was feasible even for relatively dark scenes, but excessive camera movement made good pictures hard to take.

- When a flash bulb or strobe light was used, pretty good pictures were taken, but the operation was thought to be difficult; besides, a strobe light was cumbersome to carry.

- When a picture was taken outside in the daytime, the aperture became very small due to a lot of light, hence the depth-of-field was deep and focusing not that critical. Also, amateurs tend to think that focusing with a range finder is quite difficult.

- Loading of film was often done by the camera store because people did not like to do it.

The conclusion was reached that, once these problems were solved, much better user satisfaction would be attained. Accordingly, the design targets were set as follows:

- Build in a feature equivalent to the normal strobe in a regular compact camera.
- Light weight and compactness are critical, so the size was to remain in the "compact" range.
- The price was to stay below that of a camera plus strobe.

Initially, the low price was thought to be difficult to achieve, but if the product was to be a hit, some lofty target was judged to be needed, so all the above targets were communicated to everyone involved.

There are many engineering tasks, but the points of development were clear so these tasks were addressed one by one.

The major changes from a conventional camera were:

- Built-in strobe for one-touch strobe photography.
- Range finder was eliminated and zone focus method for easy visual focusing was adopted.
- Self-timer, which is seldom used and needs a tripod, was eliminated.
- In general, a 1/125 sec. shutter speed is adequate and the strobe comes on if it is too dark, so a low-speed shutter was deemed unnecessary and a shutter was adopted with two speeds only, 1/60 and 1/125 sec., which was developed in-house.
- A pop-up type of strobe was used which is switched on only when in use to prevent a left-on strobe from draining the batteries.

As a result, the new product, the Konica C-35 EF, compared to the conventional C-35 camera, had:

Number of parts:	528 → 444	16% less
Weight:	510g → 375g	26% less
Size:	540cm^3 → 495cm^3	8% less
Price:	¥33,200 → ¥31,800	¥400 less

This E-35 EF with the built-in strobe has sold tremendously; it exceeded the initial forecast of 8,000 units per month, reaching 35,000 units per month about a year after introduction and 50,000 units per month soon thereafter. This camera gave the present-day built-in strobe its popularity and has promoted the increase in the number of family photographers.

Development of targets based on priority focusing was the major factor in this success.

6

Fact-Based Management

—Carry on discussions using data based on facts.

WHAT IS FACT-BASED MANAGEMENT?

The essence of QC is the scientific control method. Therefore, its implementation must be based on scientific observation and scientific principles. To be scientific, "factual backing" must be there.

In QC, as much as possible, judgments are to be based on facts. This control by facts is called "fact-based management." "Fact-based management" therefore means managing with data and facts, not by experience or hunches.

To base things on facts, the subjective needs to be made objective, i.e., a quantification of subject matter with data is necessary.

Of course, hunches and experience are necessary for work, since collecting data and classifying it depends on experience, and eliminating rejects requires experience to go by. However, an overdependence on experience, hunches, and gut feelings (KKD or *keiken kan dokyo* in Japanese) is very risky. Correct understanding of the facts is necessary for correct action. Based on facts means based on data. Collection and arrangement of data often leads to the discovery of hitherto unseen facts or clarification of otherwise vague subjects, which in turn results in matters being handled better.

However, QC does not neglect experience, hunches, and gut feelings entirely. Rather, they are considered one important factor in QC. Experience, hunches, and gut feelings are indispensable in discovering problems, identifying contributing factors, and generating ideas. Particularly, much experience is needed to identify and systematize all factors related to characteristics when creating a cause-and-effect diagram. But be careful, because an overdependence on experience, hunches, and gut feelings can:

- End up generating a lot of discussion without any conclusion.
- Give a false emphasis to the voices of those higher up or to those with

45

the loudest voice, and the conclusion reached will be without factual basis.

- Result in adoption of old methods or wrong means even when conditions have changed.

- Lead to too much trial and error.

A fact-finding process is given below.

How to Find Facts

Step 1. Observe work areas and actual operations.

Step 2. Determine relevant features.

Step 3. Clarify the purpose of data collection.

Step 4. Collect valid data.

Step 5. Use statistical methods and analyze thoroughly.

Step 6. Think out correct conclusions.

WHAT ARE QUALITY CHARACTERISTICS?

Measurements of partial sets of products or parts and of inquiries from customers can be a basis for action, subject to the limitations of the results that can be obtained from such data collection activities.

The entire object of investigation and study for action based on data is called the *base population,* and those objects taken out from such a base population for study of their characteristics are called *samples* for QC implementation. Samples are also called ''specimens'' or ''test pieces.''

The purpose of data collection is not to get information on these samples but to get information on the base population from the samples, so that action can be taken with respect to the base population. Figure 6.1 shows this relationship.

The important point in data collection is, on what are the data collected? In other words, how are quality characteristics selected?

- Properties and performance that are the subjects of quality evaluation are called ''quality characteristics.''

- Numerical values of quality characteristics are called ''characteristic values'' or ''quality characteristic values.''

Among the characteristics we deal with, there are those showing over-all quality, i.e., the result of certain work, and others showing the causes that lead to such a result.

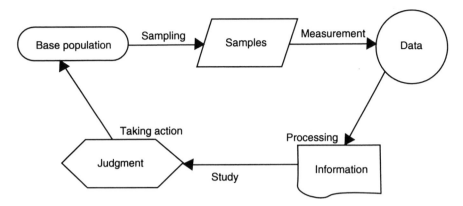

FIGURE 6.1.   Relationship between base population and sampling data.

HOW TO CHOOSE QUALITY CHARACTERISTICS

We need to select the most effective characteristics from among many, collect data on those, and tie them to actions. To control and improve quality, critical characteristics of quality, production conditions, and so on must be determined. Such selection requires the following considerations.

Considerations for Selection of Characteristics

- Check which quality characteristics of which product are required by users, and select those critical for performance and function.

- Select those characteristics most suitable for evaluation of results.

- Not only characteristics of the final product, but those of raw materials or intermediate products, can be selected to find rational requirements in later processes.

- Characteristics of assembly machinery can be selected, but selecting production conditions at earlier stages in the process of the assembly of parts and components can often be advantageous.

- There may be only one characteristic of the product or work result in some cases, but more than two often are selected, e.g., the quality characteristics of the telephone are clarity, volume, noise, and failure rate.

- It is better to select characteristics that are easy to measure and to take action on; however, do not select unimportant ones even if they are easy to measure.

- If direct measurements of some characteristics are technically or economically difficult, then select others which are closely related (substitute characteristics), e.g., if the relation between concentration and specific gravity is known, then the latter is selected for ease of measurement.

- Not only narrowly defined qualities, but also broad ones such as cost, delivery, producibility, and serviceability are to be considered.

Table 6.1 lists characteristics often measured at companies that are running QC circles. This table is a summary of an inquiry investigation asking QC circle leaders, members, or shop floor supervisors who are the readers of *FQC* magazine, "What characteristics are you using to evaluate work results?" This may help some readers who are faced with the task of selection.

PURPOSE OF COLLECTING DATA

Various types of data are collected in the workplace. In general, data are measurable numerical values. The purpose of data collection is to get information on the base population and to act on it, but the method of sampling and number of data items are different for various purposes. So it is necessary to classify the purposes of data collection. Otherwise, the data may be useless.

Classification of Data by Purpose

- *Data for status check*—What is the size variation? What is the rate of machine failures? How many customers visit the store? These data describe the present situation to find problem points.

- *Data for analysis*—The change in amount of sales by method of display, A, B, and C. The relationship between content and strength. These are typical results of the analysis of data. Factors affecting certain characteristics must be known before control can be carried out and improvements made. Analysis, and data for the analysis, is necessary for such purposes.

- *Data for control*—Is stock adequate? Is weight as per specification? These are examples of data for checking process variations. They help check abnormalities and prevent repetition of mistakes.

- *Data for adjustment*—Is the nozzle spray okay? Is room temperature okay? These are data for adjustment to desired values.

- *Data for inspection*—Is this product good? Is this lot acceptable? These are the data of judgment. They are collected at receiving and shipment inspections.

- *Data for records*—Contents of a tablet and temperature increases in large transformers are examples of data for recordkeeping. These records are kept for QA.

TABLE 6.1. Examples of characteristics for data collection.

Purpose	Characteristics	Application
Quality	No. of rejects	Reduction of rejects, steel sheet, heat treatment
	No. of mistakes	Mistakes in invoices or installation, etc.
	No. of repairs	Reduction of repairs of rejects
	Weight	Weight control of tablets or parts
	Time	Work time, handling time control
	Thickness	Control of plate, part size
	No. of foolproof	Reduction of work mistake, simple mistake
	Electricity voltage, amperage	Median value of electricity and dispersion control
	Rejection rate	Reduction of rejectable processes or returned rejects
Cost	Yield	Yield control of products
	Usage	Reduction of electricity, consumables, water, etc.
	Inventory	Inventory control, parts and products
	Energy consumption	Reduction of energy consumption cost reduction
	Personnel cost	Cost control
	Amount of work	Work reduction
	Budget v. actual	Cost reduction
	Material cost	Reduction of material cost, resins, insulations, etc.
Productivity	Production per unit time	Productivity control
	Production time	Increased production per day
	No. of days to produce	Reduction of lead time
	Yield	Improvement of yield of steel sheet
	Sales amount	Increased sales per head
	Rate of operation	Reduction of down time
	Idle time	Reduction of idle time of input/output media

(continued)

TABLE 6.1. **Examples of characteristics for data collection (continued).**

Purpose	Characteristics	Application
Work Efficiency	Actual time Setup time Inspection time Setup time Transportation time Clerical work time No. of JOB (computation)	Standard time improvement Reduction of setup of equipment Reduction of inspection work Elimination of setup waste Reduction of such time Higher efficiency of work Reduction of waiting for CPU JOB
Delivery	Rate of on-time delivery Days of delay On-time delivery rate Delay due to inspection No. of lot-out Yield Lead time No. of delayed processes	Improvement Improvement Improvement Improvement Reduction of lead time Daily yield control Reduction of lead time Reduction of delay
Sales	Amount Sales amount Profit and loss No. of customer visits Added value	Control of achievement Budget vs. actual control Improvement of profitability Increased visits to retail stores Profit control
Safety	No. of cases of scares No. of KYT trngs. (danger warning training) No. of no-accident days Deviation from max wastewater TOP Safety rate Degree of accidents Seat belt usage rate No. of patrol warnings	Prevention of labor accidents Improved safety Awareness of safety Pollution prevention Comparison to previous year, awareness Accident statistics Prevention of traffic accident Elimination of unsafe items

(continued)

TABLE 6.1. Examples of characteristics for data collection (continued).

Purpose	Characteristics	Application
Personnel	Attendance	Attendance control
	No. of proposals	Activation of work area, promotion of proposals
	No. of morning meetings	Better communication
	Attendance to meetings	Awareness improvement
	Attendance to recreation	Vitality on shop floor
	Rate of work area meetings	Better work area communication
QC Circles	Rate of participation	Improvement
	Rate of use of method	Level-up of circle
	No. of completed themes	Improvement
	No. of reports	Better knowledge of status
	No. of theme presentations	Activation of circles
	Amount of annual savings	Improvement
	No. of circles	Promotion
	No. of proposals	Improved morale
	Circle activity evaluation	Level-up of activity
Services	No. of complaints	Repeat prevention, service improvement
	Time of phone transfer	Reduction in time to transfer
	Time of phone waiting	Reduced waiting for calls from outside
	Rate of quick answer	Improvement
	Time of emergency handling	Control of emergency, permanent fix
	Time of repairs	Improvement

HOW TO COLLECT DATA

Data must be collected in a rational manner that provides objective facts for effective TQC implementation without dependence on experience or hunches. The data are then handled by QC methods to develop information on which TQC can be based. Good data are essential. The important guidelines are:

10 Points for Data Collection

1. Collect data suitable for the particular purpose.
2. Collect data in stratified form.
3. Collect data with clear "whats," "whos," "whens," "wheres," "which ways," and "how muches."
4. Standardize instruments and methods of measurement.
5. Watch for measurement errors and sampling errors.
6. Know that data always have some dispersion.
7. Make proper use of check sheets, which are helpful for arranging data.
8. Data begin to get outdated right after collection, so process them quickly.
9. Use QC methods for summarization.
10. Record date and location of data collection and name of person responsible, because the history of data is often needed at a later time.

FACT-BASED MANAGEMENT AT TOHOKU RICOH CO.

Tohoku Ricoh Co. is located at the foot of Zawo Mountain in Miyagi Prefecture, about 30km south of Sendai City. This company is one member of the Ricoh-San-Ai group and produces control boxes and photosensor drums for copiers. It was founded in July 1967 with capital of 68.5 million yen and has 1,200 workers and 30 billion yen in sales. The average age of the workers is 29 (as of 1984).

This company has recognized the need for QC since its founding, has been active in outside seminars, and has used QC based on QC circles since 1969.

However, it was faced with economic changes caused by the oil crisis of 1973. It had been complacent and had a false confidence because of its rapid expansion under the prior rapid-growth economy. Furthermore, during 1971 and 1972, the desk calculators that were its main product had undergone severe price competition and needed changes because of progress in LSI technology. Although it tried a new product to cope with this situation, the results were unsatisfactory, and in 1975 it had to go out of the desk calculator business.

While 75 percent of its sales were dependent on this product, its structural weaknesses were exposed under the stress of rapid changes in the business environment, and it was faced with a management crisis. Top management suffered from a lack of experience with introducing alternative products as well as from the reduction in production volume, and struggled to find a way to survive. As a result, it came to the conclusion that TQC was the only way out of this predicament and introduced it in December 1975. Since then, it has learned from outside teachers and from others' experiences, while at the same time trying to build a Tohoku-Ricoh-type QC.

This Tohoku-Ricoh-type QC was much talked about, but, in reality, the QC and daily work were not integrated because:

- Many repairs were the norm, and they were not standardized.
- Repairs called "adjustments" were daily occurrences.

For example: (1) The automatic insertion of components during the assembly process of the printed circuit board had the inserter often down. This was because the holes in the PC board did not match the tooling of the inserter. (2) Electronic components and other parts were scattered on the floor of the assembly area where the completed PC board was attached to the transfer tool at the entrance of the automatic soldering tank. No doubt PC boards with missing parts were passed on to the next process.

Repairs, adjustments, and out-of-procedure work were almost a habit in the shop area, and the problems were no longer seen as problems. The company came up with "3 Immediacies for Problem Solving" as its TQC slogan in 1979, and the breakthrough from the above situation would have to depend on "fact-based management" and "building-in of quality during the processes."

3 IMMEDIACIES FOR PROBLEM SOLVING

When a problem occurs,

1. Immediately go to the actual work area.
2. Immediately check the actual problem.
3. Immediately take steps toward a solution.

This slogan was based on the idea that the treatment of problems without checking for causes can lead to repetition of the same trouble and handling of problems, which without actual observation can only be half effective.

This slogan led to a correct understanding of problems, data analysis, and deployment of actions for improvement.

As a result, the company's yield has increased fivefold, its break-even point on operations has gone down by one-half, and operational profits have increased fourfold since 1979, when it was awarded the Deming Prize. It has grown into a strong company with its own unique technology among the many makers of copiers that compete internationally.

7

Process Control

—*Control the work process, not the results.*

QUALITY ASSURANCE

We must assure our customers that the quality of our products is at a pre-determined level. To put it in greater detail, we need to assure the quality of products so that:

- Consumers can buy them with confidence.
- Consumers can buy them with satisfaction.
- Consumers can use them with a sense of safety and satisfaction.
- Consumers can use them for a long time.

We can try to do this by:

- strict inspection
- free exchange of defective products
- free repair for a set period

But this is not quality assurance. Once defectives are made it is already too late. Steps must be taken and follow-up done in order not to make defectives. This is where QA is needed.

QA may be defined as ''a system of activities performed by producers to assure the satisfaction of the quality requirements of consumers.'' In other words, QA means organized activities at each stage of planning, design, production, and sale of products, having sufficient quality to create satisfaction and confidence for the period of use required by consumers. More specifically, the facts and information in the marketplace are collected correctly and are then applied to product planning, and design is performed so as to

55

incorporate this planned quality into the design drawings. Once the prototype is made, it is used to check whether the purpose has been achieved
through function and performance tests, and this quality maintenance activity is carried on through production and use. This series of activities constitutes QA.

The three categories below are necessary for QA:

1. *Quality of design*	• Run market research to determine quality target
	• Determine specifications
	• Make prototype for quality evaluation
2. *Quality of production*	• Design processes
	• Control processes to build in quality with little variation process
	• Confirm quality
3. *Quality of sales and service*	• Sell products
	• Establish service network
	• Feed back repair and complaint information to relevant departments
	• Gather voices of customers regarding quality improvement and pass it on to the product planning department.

WHAT IS PROCESS CONTROL?

The important thing here is to control the processes of various jobs and keep
them in controlled status.

Once QC is begun, the results are often rushed for quick effect and only
results are discussed, for example:

- Are defectives reduced?
- It's too bad that sales targets were not achieved.
- All our precautions against accidents did not help.

A QC diagnosis that just repeats questions on the lack of target achievement and future prospects or piles up complaints is not a real QC diagnosis.
The problem is in the processes. Only good processes can produce good
results.

Small variations in such factors as machinery, workers, work methods,
and raw materials will cause variations in the final quality. Therefore, the
causes of variation of quality need to be analyzed and eliminated, and for
this purpose process control is necessary. ''Process'' means method, treatment, order of work, etc.—the whole way of working. ''Process control''

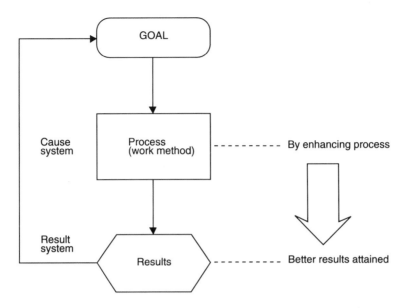

FIGURE 7.1. Conceptual diagram of process control.

means paying attention to the process and its control, rather than the results, in order to improve the setup and work methods (see Figure 7.1).

The following points are necessary for process control.

Points of Process Control

- Do not insist on conventional ways of working; rather, seek a better way with the desire for a breakthrough.

- Analyze the factors entering into differences between target and actual performance and understand the causes.

- Emphasize standardization, make standards for a better way to work, maintain them, and encourage improvements.

- Do not watch for the result versus target only, but reflect on the troubles encountered in order to improve the methods of work.

- Follow the cause of trouble right up to the source (upstream) to prevent any repetition of the same problem.

INTEGRATION OF QUALITY INTO THE PROCESS

"Reduction of defectives and good quality" are misunderstood often as "stricter inspection and checking processes."

Certainly, the major function of inspection is to check quality so as not to

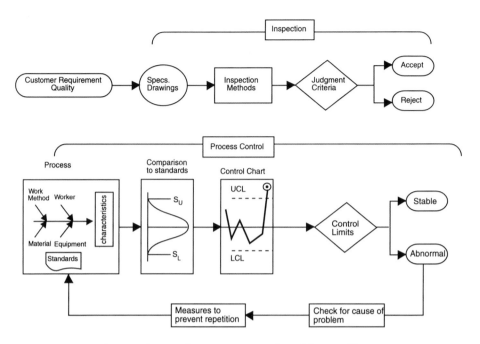

FIGURE 7.2.   Comparison of process control and inspection.

pass defectives on to customers or later processes, and one makes these judgments by comparing with inspection criteria. That is, inspection methods and criteria are set according to specifications/drawings based on customers' requirements for quality, and a judgment of good or bad is made for an individual product or an accept/reject judgment is made for the lot. Quality is assured with dispositions such as repairing or discarding the defectives.

However, these actions are aimed only at results. True, they prevent defectives from reaching customers, but they cannot reduce repairs or loss from having to discard them. Quality needs to be integrated into the process. Inspection can only remove defectives after they are made.

The function of process control is to stabilize the process so as to achieve the required quality, with stability and continuity.

To do this, go through a cycle consisting of the following steps (see Figure 7.2):

- Clarification of factors affecting quality characteristics (using good or bad quality as yardstick)
- Comparison with standards (QC process chart, work standards, etc.)
- Collection of data on characteristics
- Checking whether process is stable or not with control chart
- If a problem exists, seeking the cause

- Using the above information in revising standards to prevent repetition and to run a stabilized process for maintaining quality with only minor variations

Inspection is important for QA, but removing causes for rejection by watching the production process is more important than just removing the defectives produced. This type of activity is called "the integration of quality into processes."

PROCESS CONTROL AT THE DESIGN STAGE

The promotion of QA needs a proper understanding of customers' required quality, creation of design quality with a good QCD (quality, cost, delivery) balance, and correct design documents. All of this is passed on to later processes.

Emphasis on process was adopted at the K branch of Q Construction Co. for improvement of design quality. The remainder of this chapter describes the undertaking.

Understanding Required Quality and Deployment

Target quality needs to be built into design policy, based on a good understanding of the customers' required quality.

Improvement 1—From initial listing to a summary. In the past, customers' requirements were discussed at various study meetings but were not thoroughly understood. Therefore, the three forms shown in Figure 7.3 were prepared.

1. Chart of requirements—required quality.
2. Required-quality chart—check required quality.
3. Proper-quality chart—confirm design intent.

Improvement 2—From arrangement to understanding. Use of the above three forms showed that there was:

- Much waste of time in filling in these forms
- Checks mainly of results, with customer requirements poorly understood

The required-quality chart was revised completely to solve these problems and a new plan-policy form was prepared (see Figure 7.4).

As a result, the following diversified requirements were collected at an early stage for specific, correct action.

- Construction J was added with a pump room below the housing, but noise or vibration was a concern.
- Building H needs facade for corporate office.
- Building Z needs to be stylish because women's clothing is sold there.

Design Audit and Evaluation

Audits at the stages of planning, basic design, and actual work design and evaluation are necessary for transfer to later processes so as to achieve correct building-in of customers' required quality and desirable social and environmental conditions.

Improvement 1—Assured design review. Design study meetings were only sometimes held in the past, but a design review was now established with professionals from prior and later processes for all construction projects with a value of at least 100 million yen.

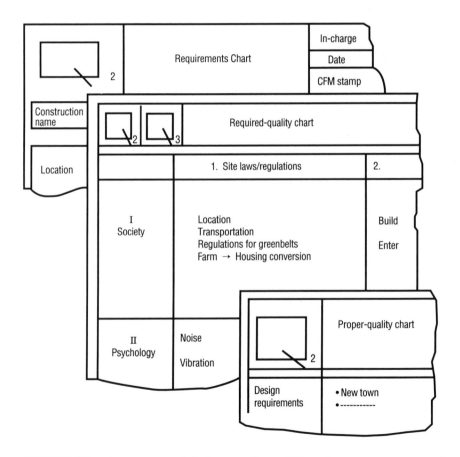

FIGURE 7.3.   Improvement 1: Preparation of three forms.

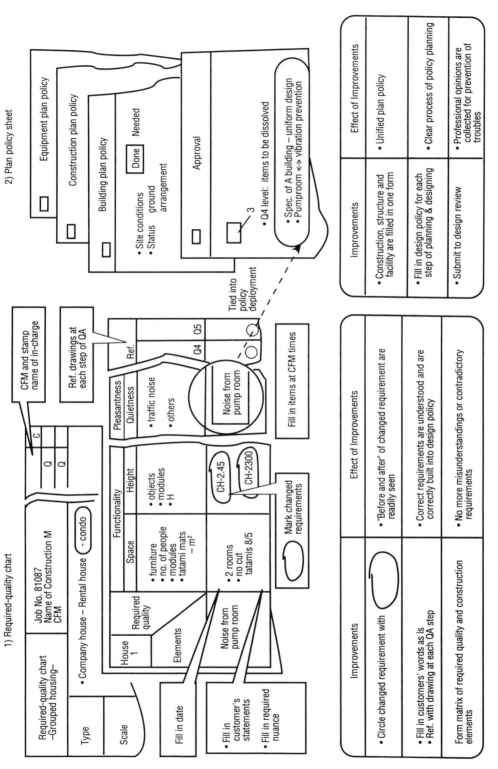

FIGURE 7.4. Improvement 2: Revised required-quality chart, and plan policy sheet.

Improvement 2—Introduction of design evaluation documents. A new evaluation sheet was prepared to assure the quality of design documents.

Improvement 3—Proper timing of design review and enhancement of subject contents. Wrong timing of design review made the contents of the review inappropriate.

Therefore, the review was separated into design review (DR) I, II, and III for each stage of the basic plan, basic design, and actual work design. An audit was mandated for QCDS (quality, cost, delivery, safety) (see Figure 7.5).

Improvement 4—Regular review of evaluation items. Evaluation of the design document was voluntary in the past and the criteria were vague. The usage rate of evaluation sheets was at a low 10 percent. Therefore, evaluation items were now quantified for review with data (see Figure 7.5).

As a result, the audit of the DR was enhanced, evaluation became a regular event, and accumulation of data from reviews of evaluation items was achieved, as follows:

- For construction D, the roof of a building subject to salt damage was treated with a material with a low life-cycle cost.

- For building Y, truck yard provisions prevented trouble with neighbors.

- For study center H, a well-balanced arrangement for a study hall, bedrooms, dining hall, research room, etc. was designed.

Summary

A series of control activities emphasizing the above processes achieved:

- Preparation and use of a "required-quality chart" for understanding customers' needs.

- Clarification of design policy by preparation of a "plan policy sheet."

- Improvement of design quality by enhanced design review.

As a result, the following effects were realized:

- No correction of design work was needed, and the amount of work at the design stage was reduced.

- Design quality matching customers' needs was integrated into the process for higher customer confidence.

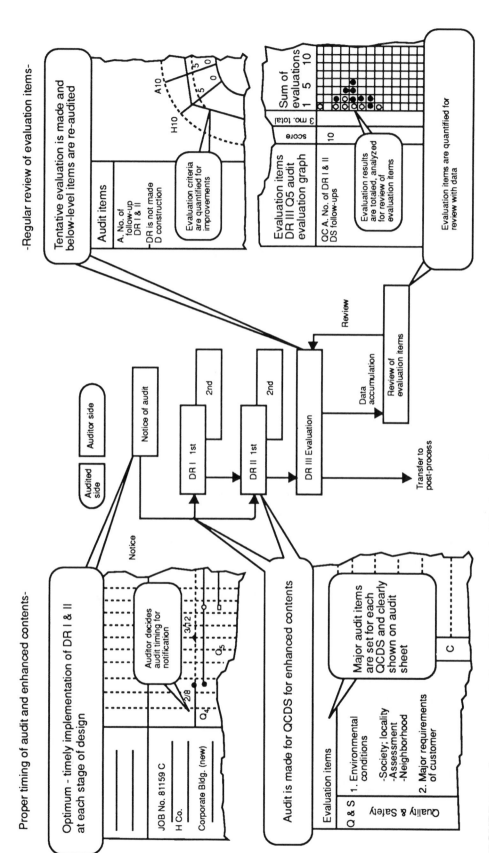

FIGURE 7.5.   Improvements 3 and 4: Enhancement of design review.

63

8

Focusing on the Customer

—Produce to meet the true requirements of your customers.

MARKET-IN

The purpose of QC is to develop, produce, and sell products and services that satisfy customers and are accepted by society.

The concept of "market-in" is necessary for this. "Market-in" means bringing the market into the enterprise. It means always to place customers first, and to bring thinking centered around the consumer into the company, i.e., to produce products and services that match the market's needs by placing oneself on the user's side.

The opposite term to market-in is "product-out," which means "to sell products out from the company"; in other words, to push out products and services produced with thinking centered around getting them to market.

Product-out worked well in periods like the 1960s when high growth rates made it possible to sell whatever was produced. But when the economy is more stable, as at the present time, consumers buy whatever they need or like, so the emphasis must be on market-in.

FOCUSING ON THE CONSUMER

Market-in means focusing on the consumer. Products must be planned and marketed with consumer orientation in order to create demand and expand market share.

There have been many cases in which poor sales resulted from lack of consumer orientation. For example:

64

- A one-touch-operation ultra-compact camera which required a special film that was too expensive.

- Colorful, modern porcelain tea kettles that gave rise to many complaints from users of a white powder appearing after only half a year of use. This was caused by a chemical attack on the coating when it was exposed to boiling over a long period.

- A black-and-white one-piece swimsuit that gave wearers striped skin because of stronger light absorption in the black areas.

- A children's tissue dispenser made of clear red vinyl with a red print pattern caused many children to cut their fingers. This was because of the poor finish of the corners.

- Some blankets, when used one on top of the other, caused the top one to slide off, or were not compatible with Japanese futons. This was because the blankets were made of 100% acrylic resin fibers which were longer than the conventional fibers of a polished finish. This made it easier for the blankets to slide in the direction of the fibers.

Consumer orientation means producing products that are liked and wanted by consumers, and this can be done by putting oneself on their side. To do this, one needs to:

- Grasp the diversified and sophisticated needs of the market and offer products and services which match those needs.

- Design and produce from the viewpoint of consumers.

- Enhance after-service and handle complaints quickly.

The following ten points should be emphasized to offer products and services on a consumer-oriented basis.

10 Points for Consumer Orientation

1. Establish a market-data collection system to collect organized and reliable data, and analyze them for use in product planning.

2. Understand thoroughly the use of products and the environment in which they will be used.

3. Be as specific as practicable regarding deployment of function and the characteristics corresponding to consumer needs, and clarify yet-to-be-developed technology.

4. Organize and standardize the new-product development system, and improve the level of development itself.

5. Perform problem predictions using FTA, FMEA, etc. at each stage of planning, design, and preproduction for prevention of trouble.

6. Relate problems discovered in all stages from development through sales to prevent their repetition, creating an enhanced QA system.

7. Know your process capability for critical quality characteristics while in the preproduction stage, making for a smoother transition to production.

8. Make an effort to control and improve processes at the production stage and aim for "perfect products."

9. Use QC methods effectively to solve various quality problems and analyze things accurately and efficiently.

10. Arrange a service system to enhance after-service.

COLLECT AND USE QUALITY INFORMATION FROM THE MARKET

To produce and sell consumer-oriented products one must know what level of quality is demanded by consumers. Furthermore, data on demand trends, competition, and marketing capabilities must be collected and studied thoroughly in order to better design in quality.

Helpful Information You Should Know:
Please Be Careful

<Leather Clothing>

i.   Dark colors may rub off onto other clothes.
ii.   Wet leather can become stiff. Be careful in the rain.
iii. Soil on suede finishes can be removed with a rubber eraser and a stiff tufted brush. Once soiled, it is not easy to clean, so please send your leather articles to a professional dry cleaner for spot removal or cleaning.

Daimaru Department Stores

FIGURE 8.1. Care instruction card from Daimaru Department Store.

This information is obtained mainly from daily sales activities, after-service, claim handling, and market research and must be:

- handled with standardized procedures from collection to use and be controlled
- analyzed from various angles to find the real demands of consumers
- classified and controlled if the information is for failure, claims, in order to determine causes and corrective actions

Public Relations in Handling Products

Daimaru Department Store has a consumer consultation corner[2a] in the store, and the complaint information collected there is analyzed at its consumer research center. Then, cards like those shown in Figure 8.1 are made and are displayed in the show windows of the store to provide information on the correct use of products.

Example of a Market Quality Information Collection System

Because Fuji-Xerox[2b] is a producer of copiers and mainly rents them, it emphasizes that it:

- offers the most suitable equipment to individual customers
- develops new products by grasping customers' needs accurately
- puts machines in the best condition for use and collects market quality information in a proactive manner to offer new products in timely fashion

Figure 8.2 shows the flow of its market quality information system, where all service data are processed and analyzed by the Technical Service Data System (TSDS) for use as engineering information.

DEVELOPMENT OF NEW PRODUCTS THROUGH A CONSUMER-ORIENTED APPROACH (EXAMPLE: MASSAGE CHAIR)

The health equipment division of Matsushita Electric Works, Ltd. develops and produces health-related products, mainly massage chairs, blood pressure meters, and respirators. Its motto is ''Building Health.''

This division develops products that comply with health principles by intensively studying the market so as to attain higher customer satisfaction.

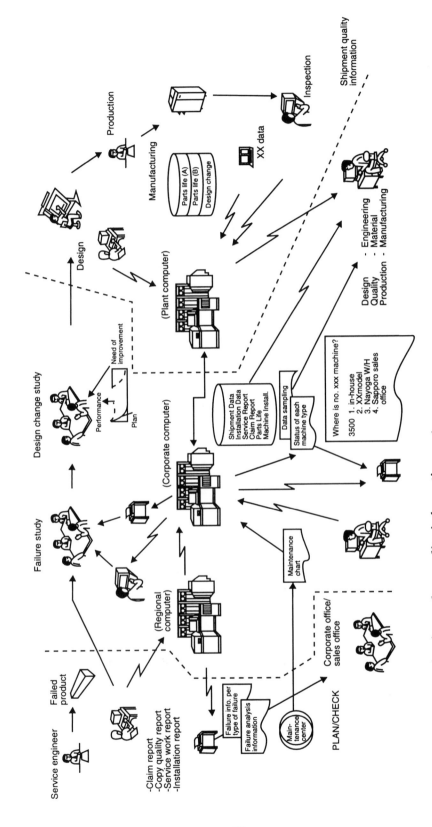

FIGURE 8.2. Example of a market quality information system.

It emphasizes the following points to create new products that will contribute to company performance:

- Establishment of individual development themes for product expansion strategies for each product group.
- Enhanced product planning process with NCP (needs, concept, product).
- Soft → Hard Conversion (system for converting user needs into engineering terms) for setting engineering tasks and quality targets to meet user needs.
- Promotion harmonized with product development, engineering, and process developments.

The evaluation made is shown in Figure 8.3 to see if QA activities are well run or not, especially in their basic structure.[7]

Figure 8.4 shows the development process for the Touchy-Feelie massage chairs (*Momi-Momi* in Japanese), which was a hit product creating many billions of yen per month in sales.[1c]

As a result of user card analysis, store reports, and home use evaluation surveys, it was indicated that the conventional Touchy-Feelie type massagers did not give the feeling of a real massage, and there was a lot of user dissatisfaction from people with back pain. So the company looked for a way to produce the feeling of professional Oriental masseurs, i.e., "strong push, strong squeeze, slow release."

As shown in Figure 8.4, they:

- Studied the principles of human physiology using the S → H conversion tool of TQC
- Arranged the relationships among factors of a finger massage (*Shiatsu*) to create a model:

  Shiatsu = *f*(movement of fingers, force, hardness of fingers)
- Attached pressure sensors to the fingers of professional masseurs to produce actual massaging curves to quantify quality targets
- Analyzed the massaging curves by computer to come up with massaging patterns for elliptical gears

As a result of this development, the automatic Touchy-Feelie massager was very well received for its superior pressure pattern and other back-muscle stretching functions, and has gained sales of a few billion yen per month.

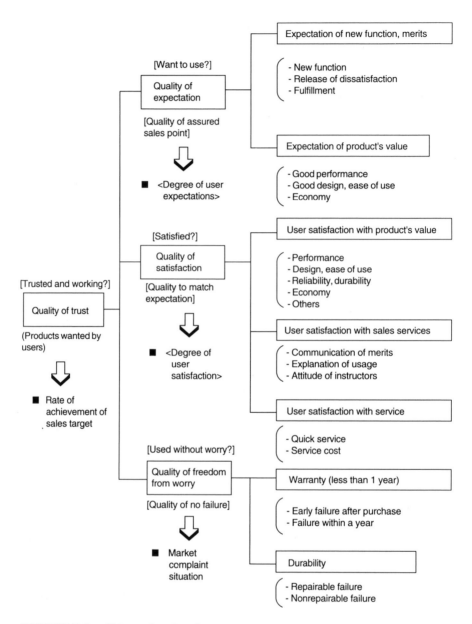

FIGURE 8.3.   QA evaluation items.

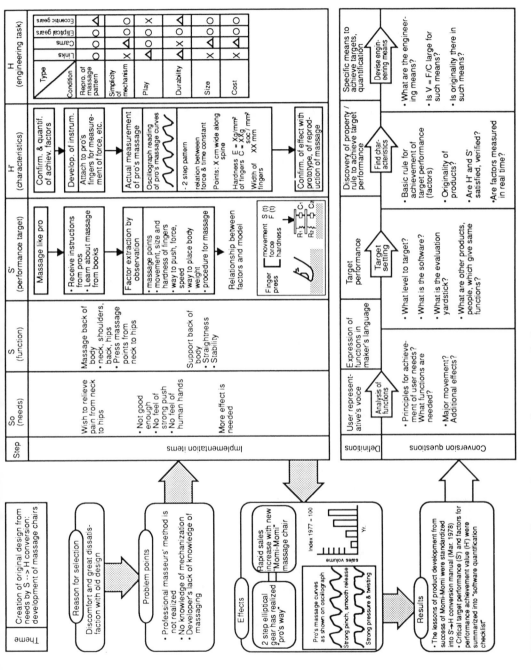

FIGURE 8.4. Development process of massage chair.

71

9

The Next Step in the Process Is Your Customer

—Do not pass your rejects on to the customer.

WHAT DO WE MEAN BY THE NEXT STEP?

This is the age of shared responsibility. No longer does a single person make things, finish them, and sell them, as it used to be.

The purpose of the enterprise is achieved by many who share the work. This is because an exclusive handling of a small portion of the load is more efficient and leads to fewer mistakes. In this age of shared responsibility, customers are no longer so specific. For example, a plant that produces sheets of cold-rolled steel does not know whether the product is going to be used in a refrigerated area, just as a plant making semiconductor ICs does not know whether they go into personal computers or into TVs.

Work is performed sequentially, with different people involved at each stage, and everybody must pay attention to what comes later. For example, the printed-circuit-board manufacturing process should work for the PC-board assembly process, which should work for the soldering process that comes after it, and so on.

There are preceding and following processes for each process.

- The preceding process affects your process.
- Your own process is your responsibility, and
- Following processes are affected by your process.

72

THE MEANING OF "THE NEXT STEP AFTER YOU IS YOUR CUSTOMER"

This concept is needed in the age of shared work responsibility. The concept means that one should work so that really good quality is passed on to those who receive products and services from oneself, in other words, to work so that the result will be gladly accepted by the next process that uses the output of one's own process.

In short, one needs to be responsible for one's own work. Once each person or department can perform its function, then products or services with a high degree of customer satisfaction can be produced.

Special attention should be paid to the following points in the "preceding process."

7 Points to Observe

1. *Know your own role.* It is important to know your own functions and how QCDSM (quality, cost, delivery, safety, and morale) are to be produced.

2. *Control and improve the way you work.* How you set up your work is important for a better job. Always try to improve your work and control it.

3. *Put yourself on the side of the process that follows you.* Reduced parts inventory is not good if the following process suffers from a lack of parts. Each process should think of the preceding and following ones, so that they may work toward a single objective.

4. *Know the processes that follow you thoroughly.* Listen and understand thoroughly what is needed, how things are done, and how things are controlled in the downstream processes.

5. *Clarify judgment criteria.* Otherwise, trouble can occur. Appearance criteria for scratches or uneven color, etc. should be judged by limit samples.

6. *Perform voluntary inspection.* Make sure there are no rejects or mistakes in your own products or work. Voluntary inspection is needed here. "Voluntary inspection" is inspection by oneself of products or services of one's own. This is voluntary assurance of one's own quality.

7. *Accurate and quick information exchange.* When trouble occurs in a preceding or following process or when a process is changed, such information needs to be transmitted to related departments for quick action or to prevent repetition. With special handling or changes in raw materials or partial changes in process, immediate transmission of such information to later processes for special attention is necessary.

INTEGRATING QUALITY INTO THE PROCESS
(EXAMPLE: MITSUBISHI MOTORS)

This case is from K. Hirashita, a foreman in the bus fabrication section, Nagoya Works, of Mitsubishi Motors Corporation.[3a] It is an example of work based on the attitude of "the next process is your customer" and "to satisfy consumers who are the ultimate customers."

*   *   *

Introduction of Work Areas

The plant is next to Nagoya Harbor and produces passenger cars and small buses, etc.

My work area produces a small bus called the "Rosa," and my work involves installing various parts on the car body. There are 22 workers in my group.

The following are features of the process:

- The work is a flow-type activity on conveyors.
- Refrigerated trucks, school buses, and left-side steering wheel vehicles are mixed in with standard vehicles, so the skills are hard to learn.
- About 750 kinds of parts are to be assembled and one worker handles some 80 parts in a single process.

Because of the nature of the work, assurance of a responsible attitude on the part of each worker is imperative. In particular, the attitude "someone else will fix it later" is not permissible.

My Responsibility

I pass on to my group as a foreman all QC information, sales performance information, and other items during our morning meetings. Problems discovered in our work area are being ameliorated with QC circle activities. In cases where we out-source, some of us visit the outside vendor's plants for discussion and guidance, and the results of such visits are disseminated among our group.

These daily activities need to be based on quality awareness, "to build in quality during our process for the satisfaction of later steps."

Integration of Quality in the "Rosa" Buses

This is based on work area improvements and QC circles. Other meetings for quality study or work area recreation are held because a pleasant work area promotes good quality.

Promotion of Improvements

So far, the rate of proposals for improvements is above two items per month per person, but this is a bit below that of other groups in this plant.

Figure 9.1 shows an example of a proposal in which suction cups are activated by an air pump to stabilize the workpiece and hold it in position.

Suggestions for improved work efficiency, consistent work results, and prevention of damage can be arrived at by running an action analysis. A 1/100 scale production line layout was made on which parts, pallets, work tables, and fixtures were arranged for better layout. This aimed to reduce waste and deviations, and has led to high quality and high efficiency.

Summary

Based on my experiences as a supervisor, I try to keep contact with my group workers from all angles and encourage participation by all for better quality. When we receive no user complaints (which are reported monthly, even when it's very quiet), group members congratulate me on the good performance of our group. This makes me feel happy. The group members' appreciation of what we have achieved in our work and our work area, without

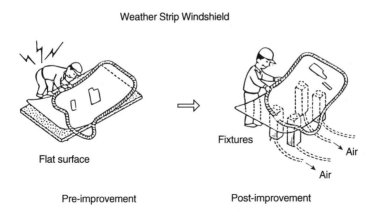

Weather Strip Windshield

Flat surface

Fixtures

Air

Air

Pre-improvement   Post-improvement

FIGURE 9.1.   Improving attachment of weatherstripping.

any need of outside pressure, and their good attitude toward preceding and following processes, are just what I hoped for.

*   *   *

ELIMINATING CUSTOMER COMPLAINTS (RICOH CASE STUDY)

This example is from Ms. M. Koiso of the "HSJ Circle" in the government sales section, Osaka Branch Office of Ricoh Co., Ltd.[3a] Her attitude of the "next step is our customer" leads to good customer service.

*   *   *

Background

Our work group is dubbed the "Government Business Co.," because we handle:

- Direct sales to various governmental bodies
- Sales activity including sales, billing, and collection
- Line and staff work for all governmental users of the Osaka Branch Office

A basic QC policy of "the next step is the customer" exists at the Osaka Branch Office, in order to improve work and to motivate QC circle activities.

Selecting Themes

Bureau B's buyer complained that "a three-day-old request for replacement of a copier lamp had not yet been responded to" and Railroad K and Cooperative D have made similar complaints.

These complaints run counter to our basic QC policy of "the next step is the customer." Therefore, the following targets were selected.

Targets

By when: before end of January 1979.
  What: complaint of "no response for request for repair."
  Action: eliminate basis for such complaints.

Investigation of the Present Situation

There are four different routes for receiving customer requests for service, with two companies performing the actual service. This time, Bureau B's complaint was routed thus:

Customer → Government Sales Section → Service Co. A → Service Co. B

except that neither A nor B did anything, with the excuse that the work belonged to the other.

We continued our investigation to see

- If the steps for repair were adequate or not.
- Why was Bureau B's complaint able to get past the management of companies A and B uncorrected? Are Railroad K and Cooperative D okay?

We called in the managers of companies A and B to join our action on this problem.

Search for the Causes

The steps to repairing the problem are determined by the person in charge, who has both experience and savvy, as shown in Table 9.1, but this could result in buck-passing, leaving the customer "in the dark."

The service company has a user list that is used to perform services, but the list is old and no updating has been done since 1976. Therefore, it missed new accounts (Bureau B was one) and small accounts, and some accounts were not covered by lists of either Company A or Company B, as shown in Figure 9.2.

TABLE 9.1. Method of routing repair requests.

Ricoh	Person in charge of service/ engineering	Request book + experience + savvy to base judgment on
	Government sales section	Experience + savvy to base judgment on
A & B service companies	The list prepared in 1976 is used as reference, and experience and savvy of veteran people in charge are the base for judgment	

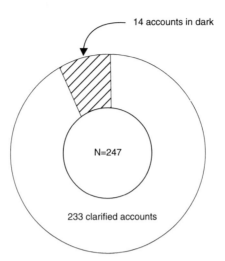

FIGURE 9.2.   Accounts to be serviced.

Taking Corrective Action

It was decided to:

- Bring these 14 accounts from the dark into the light, and make the lists easier to use
- Revise and update lists more consistently

The actions taken were:

- New user lists prepared
- Distribution of lists to service companies, Ricoh's service engineer in charge, and government sales section
- Reference lists prepared for repairs against complaints
- Review and revise lists regularly (twice a year) in cooperation with service companies A and B

New Problems

Duplication of service companies occurred at one building of one customer, which resulted from input from both the serviceman and the customer.

Sometimes Service Co. B is working on the third floor of Finance Bureau K while Service Co. A is working on the fourth floor of the same customer building; therefore, two corrective actions were implemented.

1. Re-review user lists to eliminate duplication for more efficient service.
2. Service ID labels and the business cards of the servicemen of the assigned service company are to be displayed on the equipment, to link the customer and service company directly.

Confirmation of Effects

- Complaints were eliminated, as shown in Figure 9.3.
- With an assigned service company, troubles have stopped.

Back-Up Protection

Regular checks of the user list and a method for carrying them out were standardized.

Self-Reflection

Our self-reflection, joined by the two service companies, was done because of our neglect of important user lists and neglect of smaller accounts.

The importance of information exchanged among the parties involved and of a system of cooperation to combine sales and service activities were recognized.

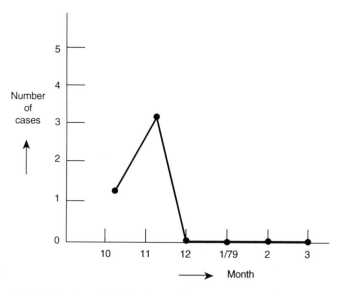

FIGURE 9.3. Elimination of customer complaints.

10

Using QC Techniques

—Don't do it your way, learn QC techniques and use them well.

SIGNIFICANCE OF QC TECHNIQUES

The features of QC in Japan are:

1. Companywide QC, QC of participation by all
2. Education and training in QC
3. QC circle activity
4. QC diagnosis and audit
5. National QC promotion movement
6. Use of statistical methods

These six items were summarized at the end of the Seventh QC Symposium in December 1968. Dr. Deming in his 30th Anniversary Deming Prize speech stated that "Japan has conquered the world markets by using statistical thinking and methods."

The following items are the pillars supporting the use of QC methods in Japan.

- Wide use of QC techniques throughout many areas of business
- High level of use of QC methods
- Use of QC methods from top management down to the front line on the shop floor

The purpose of QC is to enable companies to offer economical products and services of the quality required by consumers and assure that quality during usage. Judgments based on facts and improvements for optimum production conditions and work methods are needed to achieve this. Judgment by facts means judgment by data. Analysis of data points to ascertain hitherto unknown facts or to clarify vague knowledge based on experience provides guidance for future work.

QC techniques are the tools for correct understanding of cause-and-effect relationships, and help draw objective judgments from the complex mixture of causes and factors. QC methods are the most effective techniques to obtain as much reliable information as possible from a limited amount of data. QC techniques have a wide range of application as a tool for future quality development, improvement, control, and assurance.

VARIOUS QC TECHNIQUES

The approach of grasping factual data, of statistically handling phenomena with variance, and of acting objectively on the basis of the results, is emphasized in QC. Numerical data are important in this respect. In recent years, QC in new-product development has been emphasized, and the importance of product planning or product design is much talked about. Also, QC for service, sales, and purchasing departments is becoming an important area because of intensifying market competition.

What Are Statistical Methods?

Statistical methods can be defined as methods that induce objective conclusions through correct planning of experiments and correct analysis of the data therefrom.

Here, these useful methods for QC activities, which include analysis of both numerical and verbal data, are called QC techniques, which may be more broadly defined as follows:

> QC techniques are the methods for establishing control by discovering problems, arranging and interpreting information, analyzing factors, taking corrective actions, and making improvements.

The QC techniques are outlined below.

QC Techniques
- *The Seven QC Tools*
  1. Cause-and-effect diagram
  2. Pareto diagram
  3. Graph
  4. Check sheet
  5. Histogram

6. Scatter diagram
7. Control chart

(*Note:* "QC Circle Activities, Basics" (QC Circle Ctr. edit., JUSE Press) considers graphs and control charts as one item and adds stratification as one of the "Seven QC Tools," however, stratification is more properly a concept rather than a tool, so the above seven are here called the "Seven QC Tools.")

- *Statistical Methods*
  1. Testing and estimation
  2. Design of Experiments (analysis of variance, orthogonal arrays, etc.)
  3. Correlation analysis (single correlation analysis, multiple correlation analysis)
  4. Regression analysis (single regression analysis, multiple regression analysis)
  5. Orthogonal polynomials
  6. Binomial probability paper
  7. Elementary statistical analysis
  8. Multivariate analysis (principal-component analysis, factor analysis, cluster analysis, discriminant analysis, quantification types I–IV, etc.)
  9. Optimization-of-control techniques (simplex method, Box-Wilson method, EVOP method, etc.)

- *The Seven New QC Tools*
  1. Relations diagram
  2. Tree diagram
  3. Matrix diagram
  4. Affinity diagram
  5. Arrow diagram
  6. PDPC (process decision program chart)
  7. Matrix data analysis

- *Other QC Techniques*
  1. Sampling
  2. Sampling inspection
  3. Sensory testing
  4. Reliability engineering (FTA, FMEA, Weilbull chart, cumulative hazard sheet, etc.)

- *Peripheral QC Methods*
  1. Industrial engineering (IE)
  2. Value engineering (VE)
  3. Operations research (OR)
  4. Creativity development

HOW TO SELECT THE RIGHT QC TECHNIQUE

QC techniques include easy graph-making using sophisticated computer programs. Figures 10.1 and 10.2 show the use of various QC techniques.

Figure 10.1 is based on a study of 75 reports of QC techniques usage for QC circles carried out over two years, from January 1982 to December 1983, and reported in *FQC* magazine (No. 229-254). (In the study, multiple uses of a method in one case are counted once; for example, where graphs are used twice in one report, it is counted as one usage of graphs.)

The Seven QC Tools are used a great deal in QC circles. The so-called "three miracle tools," i.e., graphs, cause-and-effect diagrams, and Pareto diagrams, are very widely used. Figure 10.2 shows the results of the 33rd QC Conference in November 1983 and the proceedings of the Hiroshima QC

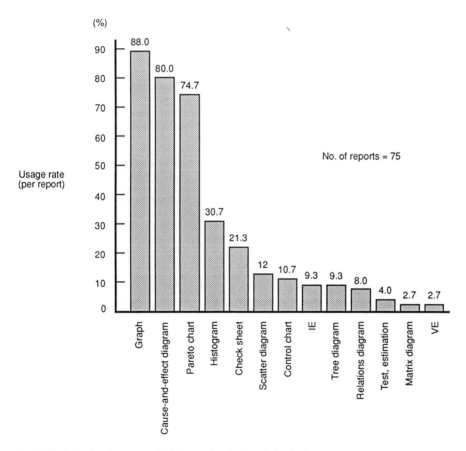

FIGURE 10.1.   Usage of QC methods by QC circles.

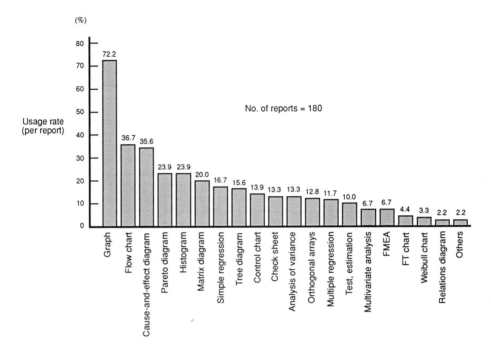

FIGURE 10.2.   Usage of QC methods by QC circles.

Conference in May 1984 (*QC Magazine*, Vol. 34, November special issue; Vol. 35, May special issue, JUSE Press).

System diagrams, function deployment, and scatter diagrams and correlation analysis are included in flow charts, tree diagrams, and simple regression, respectively. Multivariate analysis is a general term that includes principal-component analysis, factor analysis, cluster analysis, and quantification type III. Other methods considered were orthogonal polynomials, PDPC, and EVOP.

Naturally, several methods were used within one report, but the top three methods used in staff QC activities are graphs, flow charts, and cause-and-effect diagrams. However, outside of QC circle activities, statistical methods, e.g., regression, analysis of variance, and the Seven New QC Tools, e.g., matrix diagrams and tree diagrams, are more commonly used.

Using the simpler QC methods, meaning the Seven QC Tools based on such statistical concepts as base population, sample, variance, and probability, is important. In addition, use of testing and estimation, analysis of variance, regression analysis, principal-component analysis, and the Seven New QC Tools will produce even better results.

Table 10.1 is a summary of these methods for some of the more common themes.

We collect sample data not to learn about the sample but to learn about

TABLE 10.1. Uses of QC techniques.

Theme \ Method	Cause-and-effect diagram/Pareto chart/graphs	Histogram	Check sheet	Control chart	Flowchart	Test/estimation	Analysis of variance/orthogonal arrays	Single and multiple regression	Princ. component analysis/quantification types theory	Relations diagram	Tree diagram	Matrix diagram	Arrow diagram/PDPC/affinity diagram	Weibull chart/FMEA/FTA
New product, new technical development	○	○	○	○	○	○	◎	◎	◎	○	◎	◎	○	◎
Quality improvement	○	◎	○	○	○	○	◎	◎	◎	○	◎	◎	○	○
Process control	○	◎	◎	◎	◎	○	○			○	○	○	○	
Quality data control	○		○	○	○			○	◎	○				
Clerical control	◎	◎	◎		○				○	○	○	○		
Sales control	◎	◎	◎		○				○	○	○	○		
Service control	◎	◎	◎		○				○	○	○	○		
Environment/safety control	○	○	◎	○	○		○	○		○	○	○		

(Note) ◎ : very effective, ○ : effective

85

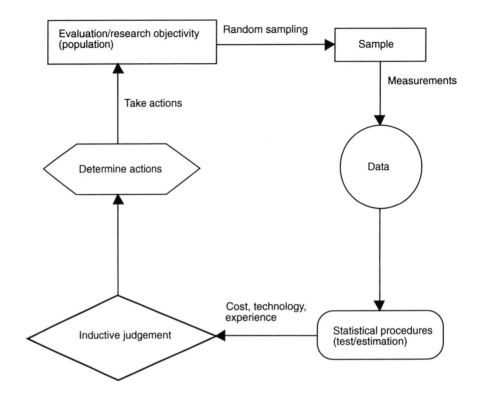

FIGURE 10.3.   Using statistical methods.

the base population. Statistical methods must be used for this purpose. Figure 10.3 shows this process. The following three items, at the very least, need to be considered for statistical data processing.

1. *Data collection*—How should data be collected to better understand the base population? Pilot plant? Sampling/measurement?

2. *Data analysis*—What method? What kind of assumptions?

3. *Actions*—How to decide on objectives after drawing conclusions with QC methods and how to acquire the economic information and engineering capability to act appropriately?

PRECAUTIONS WHEN USING QC METHODS

The following problems often come up:

- QC methods used the wrong way
- Mismatch between objectives and methods
- Insufficient tie-in to specific technology

Of course, the QC methods in and of themselves serve no purpose. It is wasteful to spend effort when one:

- Does not know how to use them
- Does not use them
- Uses them in the wrong manner

despite the fact that these are useful tools for problem solving. The precautions for using QC methods are listed below.[2c]

10 Points for Effective Use of QC Methods

1. Clarify the purpose and devise ways to use QC methods accordingly.
2. Make full use of the simple Seven QC Tools.
3. Clarify the nature of data by classification, sampling, method of measurement, etc.
4. Combine many methods.
5. Study the results of the analysis.
6. Learn QC methods well to be sure you understand them correctly.
7. Tie in with specific technology.
8. Understand the verbal data as well as the numerical data.
9. Believe that real improvement/control is possible only with QC methods.
10. Try QC methods yourself to fully appreciate them.

QC methods must be planned for a particular goal so that the resulting data can be correctly analyzed for objective conclusions. QC methods are not to be used by themselves but only in combination with specific technology.

QC methods are indispensable for process analysis, control, improvement, new product/technology development, and QA of products today. The responsibility of an engineer is fulfilled only when these methods are fully used in QC. Unless all employees are versed in QC methods, TQC cannot be established.

CASE STUDY: IMPROVING THE V-BELT ADJUSTMENT IN WASHING MACHINES

Extracting of the true factors with QC methods is very important in QC. Pay attention to the underlying meanings in the example presented in the following subsections.

Discovery of Problem and Selection of Theme

Mr. Morita is a QC circle leader at a washing machine manufacturing plant and is in charge of the washer assembly line. The frequency of adjustments of the V-belt connecting the motor and agitator was high, around 40 to 70 percent, which required much extra work and time. This attracted the attention of Mr. Morita and others.

They selected "improvement of V-belt adjustment" as their study theme with the goal of reducing work time.[3c]

Underlying Meaning: No improvement can be achieved as long as the present way is thought to be the best. A problem needs to be discovered and addressed in a positive manner.

Summary of Factors—Use of Cause-and-Effect Diagram

To adjust V-belt tension, a bolt on the motor is loosened, and the motor hinge is moved left and right to feel the belt tension (see Figure 10.4).

Mr. Morita's group held a QC circle together with people from production, engineering, inspection, and material departments for brainstorming. The result is the cause-and-effect diagram in Figure 10.5.

Underlying Meaning: Many factors thought to be related to the problem need to be arranged in a fishbone chart. Mr. Morita and other involved people used medium and small lines ("fishbones") to create a large cause-and-effect diagram for analysis of the present situation.

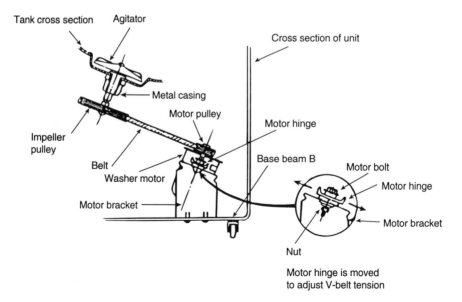

FIGURE 10.4.   Adjustment of V-belt tension in washing machine.

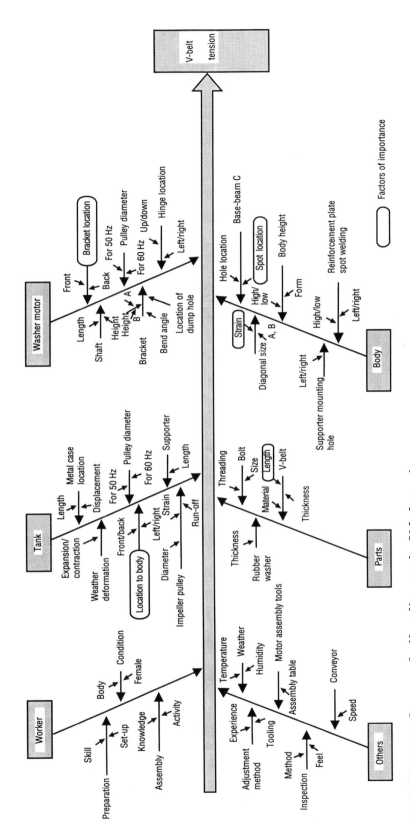

FIGURE 10.5. Cause-and-effect diagram for V-belt tension.

89

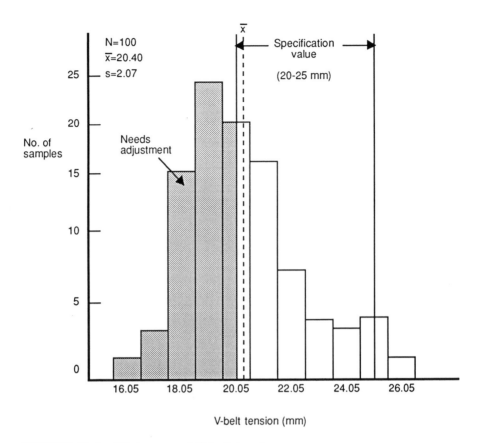

FIGURE 10.6.   Histogram of V-belt tension.

Understanding of Existing Situation—Use of Histogram

One hundred washers were randomly sampled from the production line and measured for belt tension. The resulting histogram is shown in Figure 10.6. As is evident, the distribution is towards the lower side and the variation is large, with many out-of-spec units requiring adjustment.

Underlying Meaning: Understanding of the conditions for variation of the characteristic value is necessary to discover the real causes. When data are in histogram form, the distribution is visible and can be compared with specifications.

Analysis of Factors—Use of Scatter Diagram

Cause analysis can find the culprit in the variation in V-belt tension.

Mr. Morita checked the causes circled in the cause-and-effect diagram in Figure 10.5, like the ''installation location of tank to body,'' ''location of spot welding to base frame C,'' ''length of V-belt,'' etc. These were all within

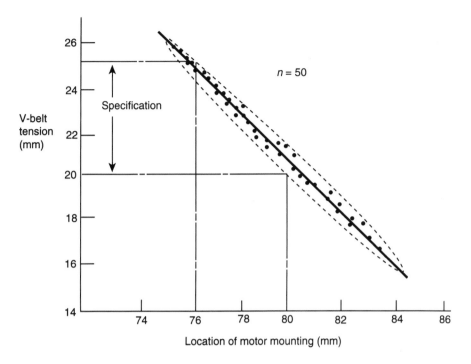

FIGURE 10.7. Scatter diagram for motor mounting location and V-belt tension.

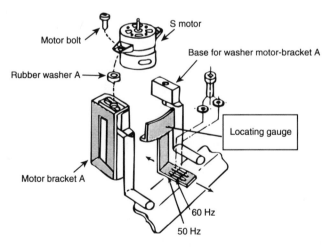

FIGURE 10.8. Mounting of motor with locating gauge.

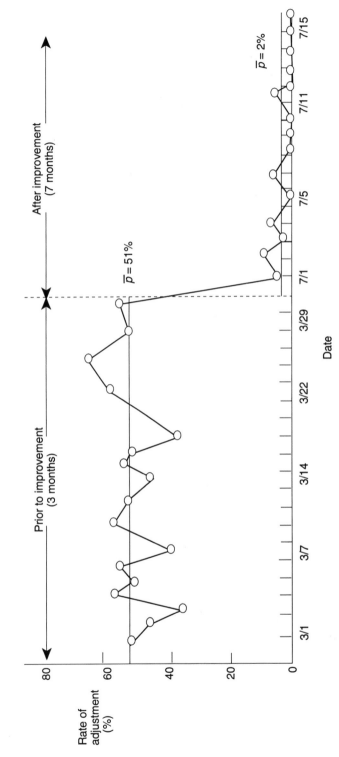

FIGURE 10.9. **Required adjustments of V-belt before and after improvements.**

92

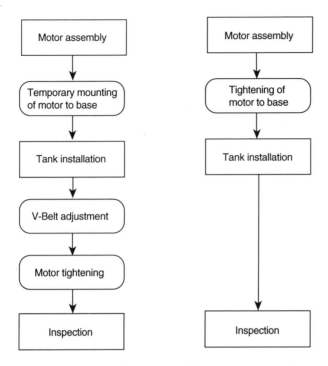

FIGURE 10.10.   Process used before and after improvements.

specifications. The motor mounting location to the bracket was the last item checked. Figure 10.7 is a scatter diagram of V-belt tensions and motor mounting locations in 50 randomly sampled units. This shows that a strong correlation exists and that a location within a range of 76mm to 80mm will do, with 78mm as the target, for getting good V-belt tension.

Underlying Meaning: It is necessary to understand the causes and effects and to take action. Mr. Morita's circle depends on the scatter diagram: the plotting of two sets of data onto one graph can provide this effective information.

Corrective Action and Confirmation of Effects—Use of Graphs

The "locating gauge" in Figure 10.8 took two weeks to prepare, and it was used to set the motor mounting location to the bracket to the new specifications (76–80mm). This tool is very effective and the previous 50 percent adjustment rate was reduced to near zero, as shown in Figure 10.9.

The process was improved, as shown in Figure 10.10, and six fewer people were needed, resulting in savings of approximately three million yen per month.

Underlying Meaning: Ideas can be squeezed out of anywhere. Giving up does no good. It was the bonding together of the group members' ideas that made this improvement happen.

In Conclusion

The means to find and analyze problems on the shop floor, and to bring about work improvements, are the QC methods. It is important to grasp facts numerically in order to eliminate the causes of interference with one's work.

11

Problem-Solving
Procedures

—Achieve improvements through persistent problem solving.

THE ABILITY TO UNCOVER AND SOLVE PROBLEMS

We often hear the word "ability." We talk about "improving one's ability" or "poor ability," etc. Is ability inherent in people? No. Dr. Nishibori says in his "QC Reminders" (Japan Standards Association), "Human nature cannot be altered. However, one's abilities can." Ability changes like a rubber balloon. To conclude that "he's no good because he's a hillbilly" or "he's no good because he never went very far in school" is inaccurate. Because ability can be changed, one must not judge too quickly.

When capability or creativity is mentioned, we tend to think of those as qualities that belong to special people. The truth is otherwise. Capability is the sum of one's actions and the result of experience and repeated learning. In years gone by it was the person with a wide and broad knowledge who was respected. But in our modern age the ideal person is one who can uncover and solve problems, or, it may be said, one who can act quickly on the basis of correct information, can grasp the real causes of problems, and can solve them immediately. This type of capability is based on a combination of varied knowledge and ability.

PROBLEM-SOLVING PROCEDURES

Our life is one of continually solving problems, broadly speaking. When driving a car, when producing in a plant, when performing as an accountant in an office—all of these activities require that we solve problems. A "problem" is the difference between a target and the current status, and eliminating these differences is what we call ''problem solving.'' This process can be divided three ways. Figure 11.1 illustrates this. The way we can enhance our problem-solving capability is to turn to problem-solving procedures and apply them appropriately.

In quality control, this process can be divided further into many steps. In sports and games we have common strategies to win. Without the skill one cannot win. It is the same in problem solving. Erratic actions will not effectively solve a problem. The common method or strategy that must be followed is an efficient mode of action that results in effective improvements. This is what we mean by problem-solving procedures.

Problem-solving procedures are a common method for rationally and scientifically solving problems. When they are followed, anybody can cope with the problems they face. We could call this ''a procedure for improvement'' as well. Figure 11.2 shows these problem-solving procedures.

Problem-Solving Procedures

Step 1. *Understanding the problem and determining a theme.*
  - Clarify the roles of the departments or sections and the goals for their work.
  - Double-check the policies and targets assigned to each work area.
  - Understand the current situations of the control items and critical quality items, and look for effective ways to improve them.

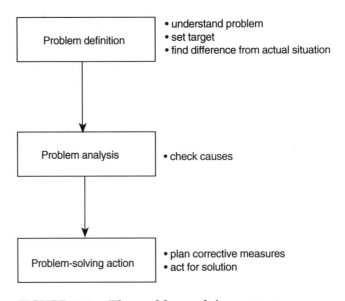

FIGURE 11.1. The problem-solving process.

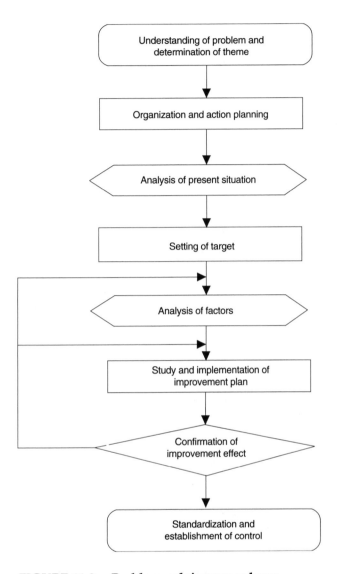

FIGURE 11.2. Problem-solving procedures.

To understand problems, one needs to do the following:

- A comparison with past experiences in order to see trends or changes.
- A comparison to the way things should be, in order to see weaknesses and find points for improvement.
- Check to see if policies are being achieved or not.
- Check against specifications and standards in order to come up with any deviations.
- Check for any adverse effects resulting from upstream processes.

- Compare with the situations in other departments or branch offices in order to evaluate one's own processes.
- Look for points of interference in the work.

To determine a theme, with a point of view toward critical items, one needs to do the following:

1. List problem points in their order of criticality for an easier determination.
2. Make predictions on the effects of what one has determined.

Step 2. *Organization and planning action.*

1. Decide on the group that will be in charge of problem solving.
2. Decide the time that is to be allowed for problem solving.
3. Set up a system of cooperation and sharing.
4. Prepare a plan of action.

Step 3. *Analyzing the present situation.*

Try to pinpoint the "values" of the effects, or effect values. Collect data on these effects in order to understand the current situation.

- What are the actual effect values?
- Are problems recent or have they been occurring for some time?
- Is the currently established average value a problem, or is the problem rather variance from the average?

Step 4. *Setting targets.*

1. Set the target that needs to be achieved.
2. Determine a yardstick to measure the effects of the problem solving.
3. Review the action plan, revise it if necessary, and determine greater details of action and sharing of responsibilities.

Step 5. *Analyzing the causes.*

1. Look at the relationships between the causes and effects from both a technical point of view and an experiential point of view, and summarize these in a cause-and-effect diagram.
2. Collect factual data using checksheets, etc.
3. Look at the relations between causes and effects using QC methods; analyze past data; organize daily data and test data using graphs, histograms, control charts, analysis of variance, regression analysis, etc.
4. Summarize the results of these analyses.

Step 6. *Study and implement improvement plans.*

1. Gather ideas and study corrective measures in order to solve problems.

2. Determine the plan for improvement:
   (a) Evaluate the effects of the plan on the target.
   (b) Look at speed, ease, and appropriateness.
   (c) Are these emergency stopgap measures? Will they prevent repetition of the problem? Or do they change the way we work?
3. Prepare or revise tentative standards and work standards.
4. Educate and train the employees in the new methods.
5. Implement the plan for improvement using tentative standards.

Step 7. *Confirm the results of the improvements.*

1. Check for improved results using QC methods.
   (a) Compare target and actual results and evaluate.
   (b) Compare the before-and-after situation and evaluate.
   (c) Look at the cost of the improvements.
   (d) Look for effect on prior as well as later processes.
   (e) Look for negative effects on other control characteristics.
2. Confirm the effects. Look for tangible as well as intangible results.
3. Repeat Steps 5 and 6 if the results are inadequate.

Step 8. *Standardization and establishing control.*

1. Standardize those effects that were achieved.
   (a) Make tentative standards permanent ones.
   (b) Integrate the work standards into the job.
   (c) Revise any engineering standards, such as specifications and drawings.
   (d) Revise standards concerned with control.
   (e) Educate and train people in the proper work methods.
2. Maintain the standards. Make sure that jobs are performed in accordance with the standards, and check on the status of control.
3. Think about the problem-solving method in order to identify its strengths and weaknesses.
4. Prepare a formal report of the results of the improvement efforts as part of accumulating the technology. Clarify the problems, record the specific technologies utilized over the past few years, run PDCA cycles, and use QC methods for problem solving.

Table 11.1 lists seven tools for solving problems in QC. Table 11.2 shows a checksheet for problem solving used at a group study meeting in a QC seminar basic course.[8]

TABLE 11.1.   The 7 QC tools for problem solving.

QC methods (7 QC Tools)	Main applications	Understand problems	Analyze causes	Check effects of improvements	Establish control
Fishbone diagram	Assuring awareness of possible causes; logical arrangement of causes	◎	○		
Pareto chart	Selecting major problems out of the many	◎	○	○	
Graph	Visual representation of data for quick understanding	○	○	○	○
Check sheet	Quick data collection and prevention of mistakes	○	○	○	○
Control chart	Checking stability of process	○	◎	◎	◎
Histogram	Viewing the shape of dispersion or comparing with specifications	○	◎	◎	
Scatter diagram	Seeing relationships of pairs of variables		◎		

◎ : very effective   ○ : used often

TABLE 11.2.   **Check sheet for problem solving.**

Item	Subject content	Attention point
1. Selection of theme	1. Is purpose clear?	1) Why is this problem picked? 2) What part of your work is most important? 3) Is this item compatible with the policy of company/department/section? 4) Is subject process, base population clarified? 5) Is the theme narrowed down properly?
	2. Is cooperation system there?	1) Is the work approved by superior? 2) Is cooperation of related departments obtained? 3) Form project teams when needed. 4) Can the cost be budgeted?
	3. Is present status (how bad) understood?	1) Are there past data? 2) Is history of data clear? (sampling method, measurement method, 5W1H) 3) Was past condition well checked? 4) Are histogram, graph, control chart, Pareto diagram prepared? 5) Are characteristic values clear? 6) Are data available on a daily basis? 7) Is measurement error clear?
	4. Is target clear? (specific action plan?)	1) When is the target completion date? 2) What about characteristic values? 3) Is evaluation criteria clear? 4) What is the expectation?

(continued)

TABLE 11.2.   Check sheet for problem solving (continued).

Item	Subject content	Attention point
2. Analysis	1. Is character/factor chart well prepared?	1) Are cause and effect clear? 2) Are items to be acted upon clear? 3) Was chart prepared with participation by all involved? 4) Do causes number more than 40? 5) Mark 0 on 10 major causes (likely ones) and (o) on 3 major ones.

	2. Are needed data collected?	1) Are good data collectible daily?
		2) Is history of data clear (sampling, measurement methods, 5W1H)? Were data collected by you?
		3) Are the data from process or post-selection or post-adjustment?
		4) Is classification of critical causes for character/factor chart made?
		5) Is Pareto analysis done?
		    a) Is loss expressed in amount of money?
		    b) Are items classified into phenomena, process, location, etc?

	3. Check against QC methods.	1) Is QC method correctly used?
		    a) Grouping—histogram, statistics
		    b) Sequential—graph, control chart
		    c) Difference—inspection, prediction, test plan
		    d) Relationship—correlation, regression
		    e) Contribution rate—Pareto chart
		2) Is data analysis proper?
		3) Is understanding of result proper?

(continued)

TABLE 11.2.   Check sheet for problem solving (continued).

Item	Subject content	Attention point
	4. Specific technology	1) Was work area checked well? 2) Was foreman asked for his/her opinion? 3) Was staff asked for their opinion? 4) Were data, specifications, standards checked?
3. Corrective measures	1. Is corrective measure clear?	1) Are corrective measures and analyses results well related? 2) Is it repeat prevention, repair only, or others? 3) Were other measures compared?
	2. Is action plan prepared?	1) Who is in charge? 2) When is trial run? 3) Is trial effect matching prediction? 4) Are related departments notified? 5) Are criteria of evaluation of result of action clear? 6) When is real action run?
	3. Is standardization done?	1) Are control points and control characteristics clear? 2) Is control characteristic controlled by control chart? 3) Are standards (work standards, etc.) prepared or revised? 4) Is the work well understood by workers? 5) Are other related departments well versed in the above changes?
4. Leftover problems	1. Have correction items been reflected upon?	1) If no corrective action taken, why? Are they going to be tried? 2) Is re-analysis going to be made? 3) Is self-reflection recorded?
	2. What are the next problems?	1) What are the next themes? 2) Back to item 1 (selection of theme).

HINTS FOR ANALYZING CAUSES

Most important of the above eight problem-solving steps is Step 5, analyzing causes. We often hear from quality-circle leaders and members that:

- They tried a theme for half a year, but still had no solution.
- They tried many things, but still no improvement.
- The theme was too difficult or beyond their capability.

As we look into the causes of these difficulties, what we often see are erratic actions with insufficient understanding of the problem. The real causes must be understood at the stage of cause analysis, so that this understanding can lead to appropriate corrective actions being taken. The following seven steps should be followed.

7 Steps for Analyzing Causes

Step 1. Clarify the purpose and the "what" and "how" of the investigation and of the analysis.

Step 2. Observe the work site closely. Use all five senses—sight, hearing, smell, taste, and touch—when in the work area to examine the current situation and to locate weaknesses.

Step 3. Sort out the relationships between causes and results. Consider the relationships between causes and results from a technical point of view and on the basis of experience, and arrange these relationships into a cause-and-effect diagram.

Step 4. Determine the effect values. There are many values to express the goodness or badness of a product or job. Determine what these values are and which ones need to be analyzed for problem solving.

Step 5. Collect data. Understand the "who, what, when, where, why, and how" in collecting data, and prepare a checksheet for data collection.

Step 6. Analyze. QC methods are tools for analyzing causes. Analyze data using QC methods in order to understand the cause-and-effect relationship statistically.

Step 7. Come up with a conclusion. Add to the analysis the opinions of the engineers or the group with the most experience, or one's managers; include cost information when coming up with a conclusion.

QC STORIES

An improvement action report is prepared whenever a work group, such as a QC circle or a QC team, is engaged in improvement activities. The significance of the improvement action report is as follows:

- It induces reflection on one's actions and gives direction to future action.
- It helps others, and ties into the horizontal flow of actions.
- It is a record of accumulated experiences and technology.
- It summarizes various processes that improve one's capabilities.
- It improves one's ability and skill in writing reports.
- It enhances the feeling of participation by everyone.
- It improves the way one uses problem-solving methods.
- It helps to improve the level of quality of the QC circle or team activities.
- It helps summarize the contents of these activities.
- It can create excitement vis-à-vis other QC circles and teams.

A formal QC story format should be followed in preparing these reports. A QC story is a story that tells of the improvements or problem-solving activities of a QC circle or team. When a QC story is properly written, it makes the report of those activities more easily understood and concise. A standard QC story format is as follows.

QC Story

1. Introduce the QC theme.
2. Give the reason why the theme was selected and target was set.
3. Outline the processes.
4. Give the plan of action.
5. Analyze the causes.
6. Study and implement a plan for improvement.
7. Confirm the results.
8. Standardize.
9. Review the effect of the activities.
10. Provide a summary of the activities, some self-reflection, and the plans for the future.

When writing a QC story pay attention to the following suggestions.

- Determine the overall structure and clarify the points to be emphasized, especially the activities performed and appealing aspects. Otherwise, the QC story will be very boring.

- Use tables, charts, figures—anything with visual appeal. One picture, as we say, is worth a thousand words.

- Be concise, itemize, and use bullets for easy understanding.

- If the title is not sufficient to convey the meaning, add a subtitle. For example, the title ''Eliminating Chronic Rejects in Electronic Parts'' might have the subtitle ''Using QC Methods to Improve the Process Capability.''

- Stay away from specialized terminology. Make it easy to understand.

- Don't forget major titles, subtitles, and appropriate punctuation.

- Put yourself in the reader's shoes. Be honest and direct.

- Write accurately and clearly. Don't exaggerate.

- Don't be too formal or use big words. This may be appropriate for creative writing, but it is not suitable for reports.

- Revise again and again, eliminating hard-to-understand words or sentences or other portions that may be unnecessary for the clarity of the report.

Presenting the results of the actions is important in QC-circle and team activities. They can be evaluated by one's managers or even by people on the outside who can help. Some hints for a good QC-circle presentation follow.

Hints for a Good Presentation

- Prepare activities using QC-type cause analysis, creative improvements, etc., to add substance to the report.

- Use the QC story to report the struggles, hardships, and great efforts of the group members.

- Avoid specialized terminology in order to be more convincing and easier to understand.

- Use charts or overhead slides.

- Use some repetition to clarify and to make it easier to listen to.

- Stick to the time allotted.

- Take time to understand any questions asked and then do your best to answer them accurately.

CASE STUDY—REDUCING THE TIME REQUIRED TO MEASURE CRUDE PETROLEUM OIL TANK SLUDGE

This sample is from the "Windmill Circle" of Kansai Electric Power Company, Inc.'s Takasago Power Station, which reduced by one-half the time it took to measure the amount of sludge (thick deposits in heavy crude oil). This was a successful QC-circle activity (from T. Fujikawa) that uses QC methods and repeated experimentation, and has produced some creative ideas (see Figure 11.3).[9]

Foreword

Kansai Electric Takasago Station generates electricity for homes and plants of the Kinki area. We are in charge of receiving heavy crude oil into tanks and sending it to boilers.

Reason for Theme Selection

Measurement of sludge is done at temperature above 60°C and takes more than two hours because of physical fatigue.

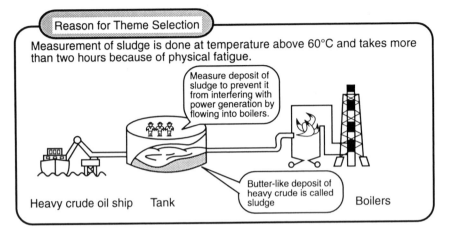

Measure deposit of sludge to prevent it from interfering with power generation by flowing into boilers.

Butter-like deposit of heavy crude is called sludge

Heavy crude oil ship   Tank   Boilers

Current Condition

1) Work procedure

2) Work time (10/1982-3/1983) (min.)

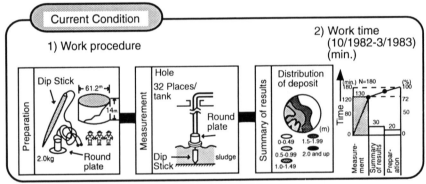

Target Setting

Reduction of work time

Present 130 min.   50%   Target 65 min.

Restraints
1. Not to increase workers
2. Not to decrease number of measurements
3. Not to degrade the accuracy of measurement

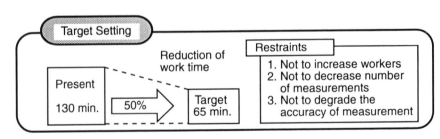

QC Circle - Introduction		Windmill Circle (formed: June 1982)	
Registration No.	174241	No. of meetings/month	2
Numbers	7 (male)	Length of time/meeting	1 - 1/2 hrs.
Average age	49	Meeting time	During and after work
Oldest	59	Theme	third
Youngest	28	Start of action to end	2/83 - 6/83
*Takasago Station operation section		Years of service: 36 yrs. (type of presentation) OHP	

FIGURE 11.3.   An example of problem solving.

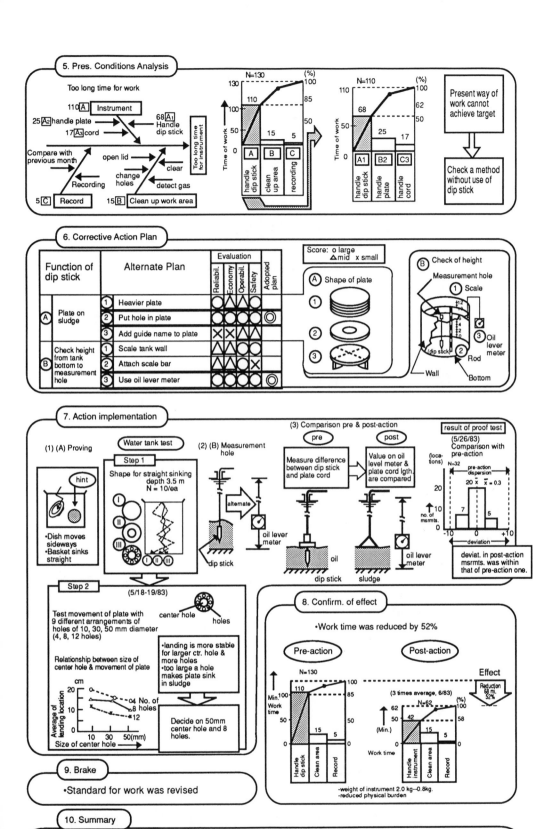

5. Pres. Conditions Analysis

Too long time for work

110 Ⓐ Instrument
25 A₂ handle plate
17 A₃ cord
68 A₁ Handle dip stick

Compare with previous month
open lid → clear
change holes → detect gas
Recording

5 Ⓒ Record
15 Ⓑ Clean up work area

Too long time for instrument

N=130

Present way of work cannot achieve target

Check a method without use of dip stick

6. Corrective Action Plan

Function of dip stick		Alternate Plan	Evaluation				Adopted plan
			Reliabil.	Economy	Operabil.	Safety	
Ⓐ	Plate on sludge	① Heavier plate	○	○	△	△	
		② Put hole in plate	○	○	○	△	◎
		③ Add guide name to plate	×	×	△	△	
Ⓑ	Check height from tank bottom to measurement hole	① Scale tank wall	△	△	△	△	
		② Attach scale bar	△	△	△	×	
		③ Use oil lever meter	○	○	○	○	◎

Score: ○ large △ mid × small

Ⓐ Shape of plate
① ② ③

Ⓑ Check of height
Measurement hole
① Scale
③ Oil lever meter
② Rod
Wall
Bottom
(dip stick)

7. Action implementation

(1) (A) Proving

Water tank test
Step 1
Shape for straight sinking depth 3.5 m N = 10/ea

hint
•Dish moves sideways
•Basket sinks straight

(2) (B) Measurement hole
alternate
oil lever meter
dip stick

(3) Comparison pre & post-action
pre | post

Measure difference between dip stick and plate cord → Value on oil level meter & plate cord lgth. are compared

dip stick | sludge
oil
oil lever meter

result of proof test
(5/26/83) Comparison with pre-action
(loca-tions) N=32
pre-action dispersion
20 x x̄ = 0.3
7 | 5
no. of msrmts.
-10 ← deviation → +10

deviat. in post-action msrmts. was within that of pre-action one.

Step 2
(5/18-19/83)

Test movement of plate with 9 different arrangements of holes of 10, 30, 50 mm diameter (4, 8, 12 holes)

center hole | holes

•landing is more stable for larger ctr. hole & more holes
•too large a hole makes plate sink in sludge

Relationship between size of center hole & movement of plate

cm
Average of landing location
20
10
0
○4 No. of holes
●8 holes
▲12
10 30 50(mm)
Size of center hole

Decide on 50mm center hole and 8 holes.

8. Confirm. of effect

•Work time was reduced by 52%

Pre-action
N=130
Min. Work time
110
15 5
Handle dip stick | Clean area | Record

Post-action
Effect
Reduction 68 m. 52%
(3 times average, 6/83)
N=62
62 | 42
(Min.)
15 5
Handle instrument | Clean area | Record

-weight of instrument 2.0 kg--0.8kg.
-reduced physical burden

9. Brake

•Standard for work was revised

10. Summary

New instrument was made manually out of waste material, which was a success, to our great joy.
This is to be horizontally expanded to other stations to the delight of many other workers.
We intend to keep our QC circle activity up under a motto of "Kansai Electric is built on quality and trust."

12

Standardization

—Create standards, maintain them, and use them.

THE NEED FOR STANDARDIZATION

The relationship between standardization and quality control is very close. Problems such as rejects occurring in the daily process, wrong payments because of an incorrect classification or calculation in a travel expense, or delivery of the wrong products to the wrong customers occur because of poor standardization. Standardization is an indispensable element for industrial production, sales, and services.

When, where, what, and how: these must be established for all members of a company if the company's activities are to be promoted successfully. Knowing them enables the control cycle of the company to work effectively. The roles and work methods of members of an organization need to be specific and clearly stated in writing.

This is the purpose of standardization. Of course, products can be produced and sold without standardization. But the variation in the work quality would be great and unstable, and the job would entail a great deal of waste and other problems. A company needs to standardize its materials, its machinery, its people, and its work methods to avoid this waste and variation, so that the results will be the same no matter who the worker is and when the job is performed.

Standardization should also be applied to:

1. The technology of a company so that it can be more effectively used.

2. The work methods in the company so that rationalization and greater efficiency can be achieved, which is part of the company's objectives.

WHAT IS STANDARDIZATION?

This phrase is often used vaguely. The following definition will help avoid confusion. JIS Z 8101, *QC Terminology*, defines a "standard" as an arrangement of material, performance, capability, orientation, situation, action, procedure, method, process, responsibility, authority, and concept for the purpose of unification and simplification, so that benefit or convenience can be attained among people who work together. A further definition then says that *standardization* is the organizational action to set standards and to *use* them, not simply establish them. So the word "use" is significant as well. In short, to standardize is to set the standards for things or ways of work and then to follow through by using the standards.

Standard specifications can be divided four ways, according to the scope of the people participating and setting the specifications:

1. *In-house standards*—Those applied within a single company
2. *Association standards*—Those applied within a group, such as an industrial association or conference.
3. *National specifications*—Those applied within a country (see Figure 12.1).
4. *International specifications*—Those applied around the world.

The major types are listed in Table 12.1.

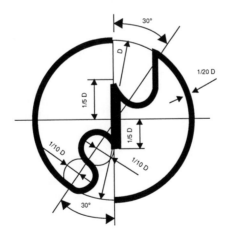

The mark placed on packaging, containers, or shipping papers when producer is permitted to do so on the designated products according to Article 19 of the Industrial Standardization Act.

FIGURE 12.1.   The JIS mark.

TABLE 12.1. Major standards and specifications.

Type	Scope of standards	Examples
In-house standards	Established within a company or plant, and applied therein.	• Engineering standard • Work standard • Product specifications • Raw material specs. • Design specs., etc.
Association standards	Established by individual association conference, etc., and applied therein.	(1) in Japan • CESM (Communication Equipment Industry Assoc.) • EIAJ (Electronics Equipment Industry Assoc.) • JASO (Auto. Engineering Assoc.) • JASS (Japan Construction Assoc.) • JCS (Japan Conduits Assoc.) • JEC (Electrical Assoc.) • JEM (Japan Electric Machinery Assoc.) • JMS (Japan Maritime Std. Assoc.) • JPI (Petroleum Conference) • JWWA (Japan Water Works Assoc.) • NK (Japan Shipping Assoc.) • SM (Japan Ship-Related Industry Assoc.) (2) Overseas • ABS (American Bureau of Shipping) • API (American Petroleum Inst. Spec.) • ASME (American Society of Mechanical Engineers) • ASTM (American Society for Testing and Materials) • FS (U.S. Federal Acquisition Regulatory Council Std.) • IEEE (Inst. of Electrical & Electronics Engineers) • LR (G.B. Ship Class. Spec.) • MIL (U.S. Military Std.) • NEMA (U.S. Electrical Mftrs. Assoc. Spec.) • SAE (U.S. Society of Auto. Engineers Spec.) • UL (U.S. Underwriters' Lab. Spec.) • VDE (German Elect. Assoc. Spec.)

(continued)

TABLE 12.1. Major standards and specifications (continued).

Type	Scope of standards	Examples
National specifications	Established by nation or group recognized as national standardization body; applied to the nation.	(1) In Japan • JIS (Japan Industrial Std.) • JAS (Japan Agricultural Std.) (2) Overseas • ANSI (U.S. Specs.) • BS (British Specs.) • CSAL (Canadian Specs.) • DIN (German Specs.) • GOST (USSR Specs.) • NF (French)
International specifications	Established by international organizations, applied internationally.	• ISO (Int'l. Standardization Organization Specs.) • IEC (Int'l. Electrical Std. Conference Specs.)

PROMOTING IN-HOUSE STANDARDIZATION

The Effect of In-House Standardization

In-house standardization is indispensable in TQC promotion. However, there are some problems, such as the nonexistence of in-house standards, the nonexistence of any system to standardize, and too great an emphasis placed on creating standards with very little compliance or use made of them.

In-house standards are defined in JIS Z 8101, *QC Terminology*, as follows: "A company standard is a standard set by the company or plant for the purpose of applying it to materials, parts, products, and organization, and to other tasks such as purchasing, production, inspection, control, etc."

Therefore, we can also explain it as follows. An in-house or company standard is an organizational act to set and use company standards with the consent of the people in the company, as a means to perform company activities efficiently and smoothly.

The purpose and the effect of company standards can be designated as follows:

10 Effects of Company Standardization

1. The technology or engineering skills of a particular individual or the company can be accumulated as company know-how.

2. Technology can be improved on the basis of the technologies that have been accumulated so far.

3. Interchangeability of parts and products as well as system compatibility are improved. Costs can be reduced and day-to-day benefits can be increased.

4. Policies and plans can be communicated more effectively within a company.

5. Information to buyers and customers can be transmitted better with the use of catalogs and specification sheets.

6. Work methods are unified so the links between various departments are improved.

7. Variation is controlled and reduced for more consistent quality.

8. Unification in regulating the work as well as improved efficiency result.

9. Labor accidents can be prevented by establishing safety and accident-prevention standards. This improves the safety, health, and well-being of the employees.

10. Safe and reliable products are produced because of better product specifications, and this contributes to the welfare of the consumers and to society in general.

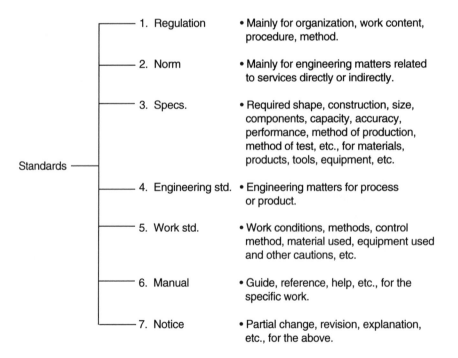

FIGURE 12.2. System of company standards.

A System for Company Standardization

Classifying of company standards must be done to promote company standardization, otherwise, (a) companywide standardization cannot be promoted systematically and according to plan; and (b) some standards will be overlooked or duplicated, making the standardization effort ineffective.

Classifying of company standards is different for various businesses, production modes, company sizes, organizations, etc., but a general system of use is shown in Figure 12.2. The details of the systems are given in Table 12.2.

How to Promote Company Standardization

Standardization is an act of the entire organization, as we have said. Therefore, it must be promoted in a companywide fashion. That is, standardization must be promoted within the circle of management policy → education/training → classification of the organization → responsibility and authority → visualizing problems → process analysis → process improvement → standardization → process control → handling complaints → quality audit.

The process for company standardization is:

1. Establishing company standards

2. Implementing the company standards

3. Revising or deleting company standards

These three steps can be broken down further into the critical processes that are laid out in Figure 12.3.

Standards differ by company or plant, type of industry, size of operation, and so forth. Therefore, the company's long-term vision and consideration of present circumstances are necessary in order to determine specific standardization policies that are timely and appropriate to one's situation. Table 12.3 summarizes the methods for company standardization. Checkpoints for studying standardization are as follows:

Checkpoints for Standardization

- Is a companywide system ready for standardization?
- Are conditions prepared for standardization?
- Is the method of establishing changes to standards prepared?
- Are the purposes of the standards clear?
- Is an accumulation of technology being planned?

TABLE 12.2. Classification of company standards.

Major classification	Medium classification	Minor classification	Subject contents	Coverage	Authority to establish	Prepared by/Controlled by
Regulations	Basic regulation	Various general rules for overall quality	Basic system of regulations and method of administration	Covers all regulations	Operation's chief	
	Organization regulation	Committees, etc., for overall quality	Basic items of organization, administration of committees, etc.	Covers work regulations	Operation's chief	
	Work regulation	Work control regulation	Method of regulation by main department in-charge and roles of related depts. & flow of work	Covers work regulations		
		Work regulation	Work execution according to work control regulation, practical methods, order of procedure	—	Dept. head Plant manager	Section chief in charge
Norms	Regulation regarding design	Product norm	Ratings, material used, construction, performance, durability, test method, i.e., basic items to be met by product	Covers all other norms and product specifications	Operation's chief	Head of design (Engineering dept. head approval)
		Part norm	Ratings, material used, construction, performance, durability, test method, i.e. basic items to be met by parts			
		Material norm	Components, strength, properties, test methods, etc., to be met by material	Covers specifications for parts, material, packaging, etc.		
		Durability norm	Durability of product, durability of open/shut part, driven parts, etc.			
		Packaging norm	Construction, strength, display, test method to be met by packaging			
		Surface treatment norm	Property, appearance, durability, test method to be met by surface finish			
		Size norm	Regular tolerance applied to pressed parts, resin part, etc.			
		Display norm	Display for products			
	Test methods	Product test norm	Product test procedure, conditions, method, instrument, etc., for unification of tests	When adopted into other norm or specification same coverage as such	Operation's chief	Head of design (Engineering dept. head approval)
		Part test norm	Product test procedure, conditions, method, instrument, etc., for unification of tests			

Standards

Specifications

Group	Item	Description	Regulate specification preparation for product, parts, material		
Design specifications	Plan specifications	For plan purpose, target, schedule, policy		Operation's chief	Head of design
	Design specifications	Specific quality target for design prototype		Engineering dept. head	Head of plan
Specification for products, parts, and materials	Product specifications	Name, part no., ship to, rating, feature, quality, etc., for each product	Covers parts, material, packaging, inspection, production specifications	Plant manager	Design room head
	Part detail list, assembly chart	Part of product specifications, for assembly parts			
	Part specifications (drawings)	Type, classification, size, treatment, machining, performance, durability, etc., for each part	Covers inspection, production specifications	Engineering department head	
	Package specifications	Package, structure, method, etc., for product packaging			
	Color specifications	Color of products			
	Material specifications	Thickness, cut size, mechanical property, etc., of material used		Plant manager	Section head in charge
Inspection specifications	Finished product inspection specs.	Items, accept/reject criteria/method, etc., for each product	Covers production specifications	Plant manager	Section head in charge
	Part inspection specifications	Items, accept/reject criteria/method, etc., for each part		Section head	Section head in charge
	Material receiving inspect. specs.	Items, accept/reject criteria/method, for material received		Plant manager	Section head in charge
Production specifications	Production method specifications	Method of assembly, conditions, etc.	Covers work instructions	Plant manager	Section chief in charge
	Process control standards	Control items, method, criteria, etc., for each process			
	Adhesive coating specifications	Name of adhesive for each part adhered		Engineering dept. head	Design room head
	Work instructions	Method, safety, quality, efficiency, etc., for each worker and equip.	—	Section head	Foreman-group head in charge
Equipment specifications	Facility specification drawings	Material, construction, accuracy, performance, etc., of tooling, machines, gauge, metal dies, including drawings. Also includes owner's operation manual when required.	—	Section head	Chief in charge
	Tooling specification drawings				
	Metal dies specification drawings				
	Gauge specification drawings				

Manual

Group	Item	Description			
Manuals	Manuals for work	Manuals for accurate & efficient work at departments		Section head	Person in charge

117

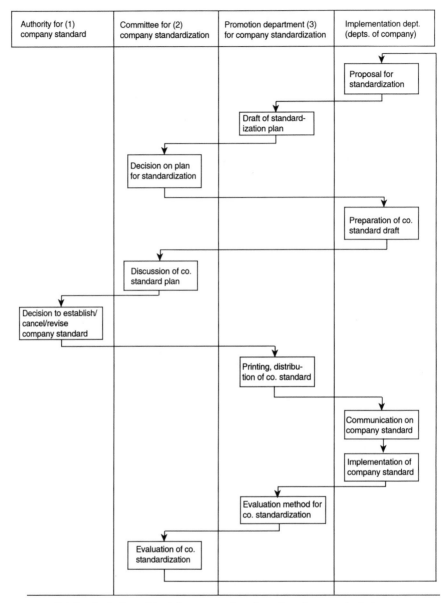

Authority for (1) company standard	Committee for (2) company standardization	Promotion department (3) for company standardization	Implementation dept. (depts. of company)

(Notes)
1) In-charge delegated or managers depending on type of company standard
2) Committee with functions to standardize, such as QA committee or standardization committee
3) Department in charge as office of company standard promotion committee

FIGURE 12.3. Procedure for implementation or revision of company standards.

TABLE 12.3. Procedures for company standardization.

No.	Step	Implementation item
1	Prepare system for standardization	(A) Approach top management or managers (B) Decide on those who are central for standardization (C) Work for participation by all

2	Plan for standardization (PLAN)	(A) Design of standardization system
		  (a) Clarify the purpose of standardization
		  (b) Design outline
		  (c) Design details
		  (d) Select practical plans
		  (e) Design procedures for implementation
		(B) Elements of standardization system
		  (a) Written purpose for standardization
		  (b) Decision on standardization organization
		  (c) Decision on company standard system
		  (d) Decision on clerical handling of standardization
		  (e) Education in standards

3	Administration of standardization (DO)	(A) Plan for administration
		  (a) Classification and numbering of standards
		  (b) Method of handling of standards
		  (c) Issue/revise/cancel standard
		  (d) Method to collect and distribute various data
		(B) Cautions for standard-making
		  (a) Standard itself is a system
		  (b) Think about cost
		  (c) Should be vertically arranged
		  (d) Look for improvement
		(C) Cautions for usage
		  (a) Implement according to standard
		  (b) Devise better way to use
		  (c) Use it for education
		  (d) Combine training for standards covering various departments

4	Evaluation of standardization (CHECK)	(A) Evaluate overall result (B) Evaluate per department

- Are standards being used?
- Are statistical methods being used?
- Are the contents of the standards complete?
- Is the task achievable?
- Is the task interpreted by everyone in the same manner?
- Are there contradictions with other standards?
- Can the standards be complied with?
- Are they in an easy-to-use form?

THE PURPOSE AND CONTENTS OF WORK STANDARDS

What Is a Work Standard?

Each job requires its own way of working, whether it is parts assembly, machining, inspecting materials or products, or even bookkeeping. Skilled people are able to perform a job in a much shorter period of time than it would take a newcomer. But even among the most skilled, the way people work can differ, with a variety of efficiencies and results. In order to achieve 100 percent acceptability, the following points must be adhered to.

1. Determine the correct way to work.
2. Work accordingly, and steadfastly.
3. Make improvements all the time.

This is the correct way to work and this is defined as the work standard. According to JIS Z 8101, *QC Terminology*, a work standard is defined as: "The criteria related to work conditions, methods, control methods, materials used, equipment used, and other precautions."—in other words, "the regulation of the correct way of working and of actions for production of good products at low cost, quickly and easily."

A variety of names can be assigned to work standard sheets, depending on the plant or the contents required. They could be called work standard sheets, work procedure sheets, work instruction sheets, a work manual, a work guidance sheet, etc.

The Purpose of Work Standards

The purposes of work standards can be classified with a view toward preparing the standards.

The Purposes of Work Standards

- To regulate work methods and actions
- To arrange in proper order instructions, guidance, and supervision, resulting in smooth work
- To clarify the sharing of work responsibility and to take care of any problems or contradictions that might arise
- To clarify the responsibility and authority of each work department
- To make work methods more uniform, making them easier to control and improve
- To pinpoint consistencies that are found in repetitive work
- To make education and training of the workers easier
- To assure that people work correctly in as short a time as possible
- To accumulate engineering and technological information

The Contents of a Work Standard

These could be defined as:

1. *Aim*—Is it to be a work manual, a procedural manual, or an instruction manual?
2. *The type of company or production process*—Is it a machine industry, chemical industry, assembly, equipment; continuous production or batch production?
3. *Who does it?*—Is the person the head of a group or foreman, or a job supervisor, a skilled worker, or perhaps even a newcomer?

The contents can be:

- A detailed description of the necessary items in the overall process
- A simple description of hints or precautions for the job using pictures or illustrations

It is important that the work standards be prepared through the mutual efforts of those who issue them and those who use them, so that they can be easy to use and comply with. Descriptions should be itemized with figures and tables. The contents of the work standards should be, generally speaking, as follows:

- Scope of application
- Raw materials/parts to be used

- Equipment/facility to be used
- Methods, conditions, and precautions
- Amount of time allotted for work
- The unit cost for the work
- Control items and control methods
- Norms
- What to do in emergencies
- Maintenance, checking of equipment and tools
- Types of workers and capabilities

Examples of work standards are shown in Figures 12.4 through 12.7. Figures 12.5 and 12.6 are those used in the Hikone Plant of Matsushita Electric Works. Each person in charge of a production line prepares "My Control Points," as shown in Figure 12.6, based on the work procedures in Figure 12.5 that are prepared by the production staff. The company head of the TQC promotion department, Mr. K. Okuda, is very strict about quality aims and wants to maintain their world-class quality. He says, "This makes the detailed work with critical points possible, and awareness of standards enhances the interpretation so that our quality can be assured."

Conditions for Work Standards

The following requirements should be satisfied in work standards and their preparation.[3e]

- To be compatible with the purpose.
- To regulate not results but the causes in the process.
- To be as specific as possible.
- To be appropriate for everybody.
- To be practical.
- Do not try to be perfect from the beginning.
- Pick up and integrate opinions from the shop floor.
- Always revise.
- Be clear about the critical work points.
- Be clear with regard to responsibility and authority.
- Try to avoid contradicting related or other standards.
- Ensure that the standards are recognized by related departments.
- Must be in writing.

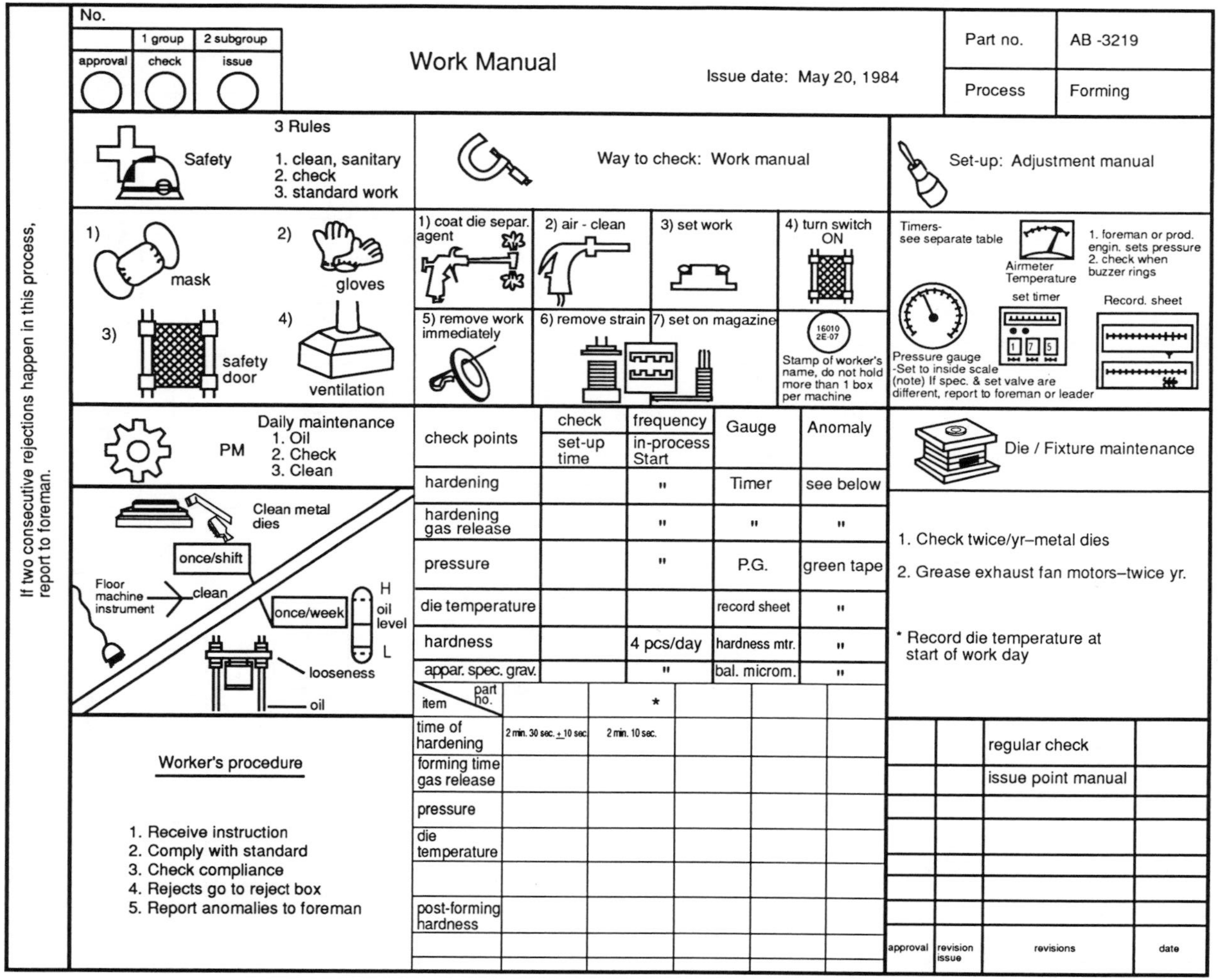

No.

approval	check	issue
○	○	○

1 group	2 subgroup

Work Manual

Issue date: May 20, 1984

Part no.	AB-3219
Process	Forming

3 Rules

Safety
1. clean, sanitary
2. check
3. standard work

1)
2) gloves
mask
3)
4) ventilation
safety door

Daily maintenance
1. Oil
2. Check
3. Clean

PM
Clean metal dies
once/shift — clean
Floor machine instrument
once/week
oil level H L
looseness
oil

Way to check: Work manual

1) coat die separ. agent
2) air - clean
3) set work
4) turn switch ON

5) remove work immediately
6) remove strain
7) set on magazine

Stamp of worker's name, do not hold more than 1 box per machine

check points	check set-up time	frequency in-process Start	Gauge	Anomaly
hardening			Timer	see below
hardening gas release		"	"	"
pressure		"	P.G.	green tape
die temperature			record sheet	"
hardness		4 pcs/day	hardness mtr.	"
appar. spec. grav.		"	bal. microm.	"

item part no.				
time of hardening	2 min. 30 sec. ±10 sec	2 min. 10 sec.	*	
forming time gas release				
pressure				
die temperature				
post-forming hardness				

Worker's procedure

1. Receive instruction
2. Comply with standard
3. Check compliance
4. Rejects go to reject box
5. Report anomalies to foreman

Set-up: Adjustment manual

Timers— see separate table

Airmeter Temperature
set timer

Pressure gauge
-Set to inside scale (note) If spec. & set valve are different, report to foreman or leader

1. foreman or prod. engin. sets pressure
2. check when buzzer rings

Record. sheet

Die / Fixture maintenance

1. Check twice/yr–metal dies
2. Grease exhaust fan motors–twice yr.

* Record die temperature at start of work day

regular check

issue point manual

approval	revision issue	revisions	date

If two consecutive rejections happen in this process, report to foreman.

FIGURE 12.4. Work manual for forming process.

Work procedure	(Process Name) Assembly, constant speed exhaust valve (1/2)		Part No.	EW 213
	(P.1/2)		No.	Panasonic EW 213 Z$_2$-01

Procedure	Points	Cautions	Quality	Efficiency	Safety
1. Insert valve case into fixture					
2. Insert rubber part A from top of valve case and press using fixture	2-1 Confirm if center hole of rubber part A is open so as to permit insertion of rubber part B		○		
	-2 Confirm direction of insertion of A (correct) (wrong)		○		
3. Insert wire ring into valve case with tweezers	3-1 Confirm alignment of wire ring with valve case		○		
4. Press in rubber part B and valve support, then insert it into valve case	4-1 Confirm closing of center hole of rubber part B so as to prevent insertion of A		○		
5. Place holding spring on valve	5-1 Confirm angle of holding spring		○		
6. Put O-ring in tube joint, attach it to two fingers	6-1 Confirm alignment of tube joint with two fingers of valve case		○		
7. Remove from fixture and insert O-ring into valve case	7-1 Confirm bottoming of valve case		○		

8. "L" pipe
6.2 O-ring (P10)
6.1 tube joint
7. O-ring (PS)
4.2 valve support
4.1 rubber part B
5 holding spring
3 ring
2 rubber part A
(1) valve case
0 fixture

<Constant speed valve assembly>

Regular check (every 3 months)	No.	Plan date	Work date
	(1)	6/82	8/82
	(2)	9/82	11/82
	(3)	12/82	1/83
	(4)	3/83	4/83
	(5)	6/83	7/83
	(6)	9/83	9/83
	(7)		
	(8)		
	(9)		
	(10)		
	(11)		

Issue	Mar. 1, 1982	Approval ○	Issue ○	Check ○	Draft ○

Standard time	Freq	Date		Name	Spec. accuracy	Control No.		1	"L" pipe	1
	△	/	Machine,	Fixture				1	O-ring (PS)	1
	△	/	Fixture, instrument, checker	Tweezers				1	Tube joint	1
	△	/						1	Holding spring	1
	△	/						1	O-ring (P10)	1
	△	/							Part name	No.

History of change	Freq	Date	Reason for change	Approval	Check	Change	Upper class std. change	Lower class std. change
	△		Change rubber part C to A and B	○		○		
	△		Panasonic spec.	○○		○○		
	△							

Authority for this standard	Foreman	(Note) In case of change, always request changes in upper & lower class standards & confirm such changes	Upper class std.	Control process chart	Lower class std.		

FIGURE 12.5. Work procedure sheet.

124

My control points	(Process name) Assembly, constant speed exhaust valve (P 1/2)		Part No.	EW 213
			No.	K_2 –01 Panasonic

Location	Caution	Result	Critical Points
1. Insertion of rubber part A into valve case	2 Rubber part A (correct) 4-1 Rubber part B (wrong) 1 Valve case Insert	• No air is exhausted	• 100% visual check of opening of center hole of rubber part • Color I.D. boxes for rubber parts A and B
2. Insertion of ring to groove of valve case	3 Metal ring 1 Valve case Ring is not inserted into groove	• Uneven exhaust	• 100% visual check insertion
3. Insertion of rubber part B to valve support and to exhaust case	4-2 Valve support 4-1 Rubber part B Insertion with support part at bottom 1 Valve case	• Uneven exhaust	• Confirm 100% visually bottom location of rubber part B to valve case
4. Attach tube joint to valve case	6 Tube joint (Correct) (Wrong) 1 Valve case Finger is not aligned	• Valve block disintegrates	• Visual check of alignment of tube joint to two fingers of valve case
5. Insertion of O-ring to valve case	7 O-ring Forgotten insertion of O-ring 1 Valve case	• Air leakage	• Visual confirmation of O-ring into valve case

				No.	Plan date	Work date
(Remarks)	Emergency handling	• In case of anomaly, report to foreman immediately and receive instructions.	Regular check (every 3 months)	①	6/82	8/82
				②	9/82	9/82
				③	12/82	12/82
				④	3/83	3/83
				⑤	6/83	6/83
				⑥	9/83	9/83
				⑦		
				⑧		
				⑨		
				⑩		
				⑪		

• Color I.D. of sampling method is easier to use (in-process sampling–before shift–100%)

| Issue | Mar. 26, 1982 | Approval | ◯ | Issue | ◯ | Check | ◯ | Draft | ◯ |

Standard time	Frequency	Date	Reason for change	Approval	Check	Change	U.C. std. change	L.C. std. change
	⚠	9/24/83	Panasonic spec.	◯		◯		
	△							
	△							
	△							
	△							
	△							

| Authority for this standard | Foreman | (note) In case of change, always request changes in upper &lower class. standards & confirm such changes | Upper class. std. | control process chart | Lower class. std. | | |

FIGURE 12.6. My control points.

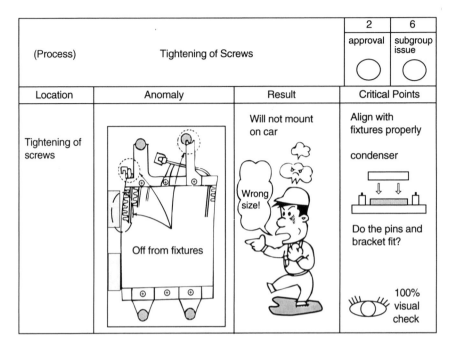

			2	6
			approval	subgroup issue
(Process)	Tightening of Screws		◯	◯
Location	Anomaly	Result	Critical Points	

FIGURE 12.7.   Work standard, showing critical points.

- There must be contingency plans.
- They must be easy to read and to use.
- They must be prepared with the understanding that they will need to be complied with.
- They must not be a collection of "don'ts."

CASE STUDY—REDUCING THE NUMBER OF REWORKS THROUGH WORK STANDARDS

As mentioned above, the purpose of standardization is not just to standardize but to achieve quality assurance. The example of the Osaka branch office of Kajima Corporation shows the success of work standards in warehouse construction (see Figure 12.8).

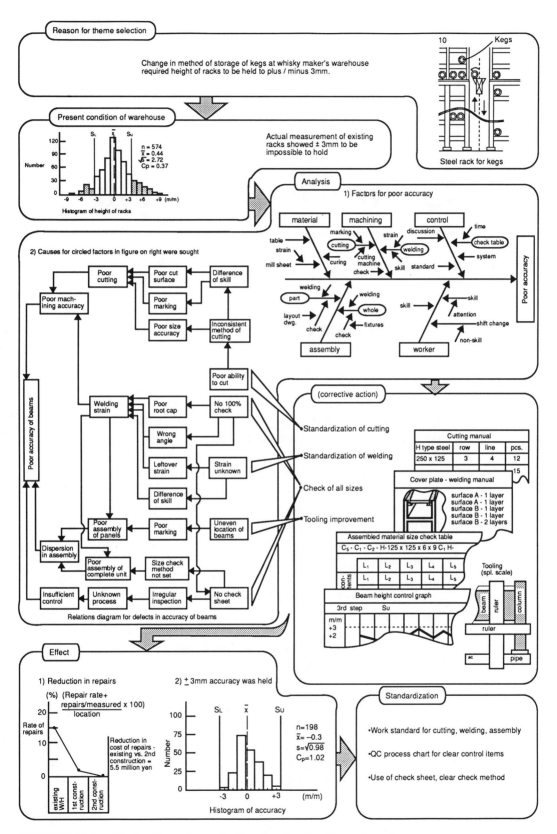

FIGURE 12.8. Reduction of repairs by standardization of work.

127

13

Control of Variation

—Look for variation and find the causes for it.

ALL DATA SHOW SOME VARIATION

We strive to produce good products every day; however, there are some variations in product quality (quality characteristics) that always seem to occur, even when the products are made by the same process, by the same worker, by the same work standard, with the same materials and equipment. Whether the product is concrete, parts, a daily sales amount, relay timing, or operating temperatures in bimetals, it will have some variation. This is because the data we get are affected not only by the effects of handling, but also by changes in the environment or in processes that cannot be controlled. Variation is inevitable in view of statistics as well. The point is to confine this variation to within a permissible range. In other words, ''watch for variation and control it'' is the concept of variation control. The following points describe this control.

1. Data will be distributed around a certain value.
   - Form of distribution
   - Mean of distribution, or $\bar{x}$
   - Variance of distribution (standard deviation, s) needs to be obtained. Histograms are useful, as well.
2. There are many causes for variations in quality originating in processes, but these can be classified into the following two:
   - Those due to chance causes—they happen even with standardized materials and work methods; they are inevitable.
   - Those due to causes that can be identified—they occur because of noncompliance with standards or inadequate standards; these are impermissible.

128

Controlling a process means permitting those variations that occur as the result of chance causes but eliminating the others by taking actions to ensure that the variation is not repeated. Control charts are used to separate the two types of variations and to analyze and control processes.

A PROCESS CAPABILITY STUDY

What Is Process Capability?

The point of quality control at a plant is to understand process capability in order to maintain or improve it. Determination of process capability is first needed for proper quality and design. JIS Z 8101 (*QC Terminology*) defines process capability as "the limit of capability that is rationally achievable given certain needed results, using a stable process." In other words, process capability indicates what degree of quality can be realized when a given work standard is applied. The variation in products produced under a predetermined process and under predetermined work conditions is of particular importance here.

In general, the causes that affect product quality come under "the 4 Ms," that is, material, machine, method of work, and man (people). The upper limit of quality achievable by a process, based on these 4 Ms at the present level of technology and economy, is called process capability. It can also be defined as capability with regard to the quality of the process when process standardization is adequate and assignable causes of variation are removed, and the process is stabilized.

The Purpose of a Process Capability Study

Process capability must be adequate to the task of producing products and services that can be bought by consumers with satisfaction. Thus, process-capability improvement needs to be made if the process is insufficient for achieving this goal, and it must be maintained if it is adequate for achieving this goal.

In any case, understanding a process is necessary to promote QC activities, and studying it is called a process capability study. The purposes of such studies for various departments are as follows.

Purposes of Process Capability Studies

- *Design department*—Basic information for determining tolerances or engineering targets
- *Production engineering department*—Information on which to base the

setting and changing of process designs, machine tooling designs, machining conditions, etc.

- *Production department*—The basic information for a control plan for process quality, determining the method of process control, process analysis, etc.

- *Inspection department*—Reference information for setting inspection methods

- *QC department*—An evaluation base for production- or shipping-quality evaluation

- *Purchasing department*—Reference data for selecting suppliers or a confirmation date, or for evaluating purchased products

- *Sales department*—Reference information for determining selling prices, etc.

How to Study

Basically, follow the method below.

Procedures for Studying Process Capability

Step 1. Clarify the purpose of the study and application of results.

Step 2. Determine the quality characteristics and the scope of the study.

Step 3. Standardize the 4 Ms, which are the factors that will change for quality.

Step 4. Collect data according to the study plan.

Step 5. Prepare an $\bar{x}$–R control chart to check stability of the process.

Step 6. Prepare a histogram and calculate the process capability index (C_p, C_{pk}).

Step 7. Check the current process capability; maintain it if it is satisfactory or improve it if it is not.

More specifically, the procedures in Figure 13.1 should be followed. Tables 13.1 and 13.2 show (a) the methods of calculating the process capability index, C_p, including when to consider the process trend using C_{pk}; and (b) judgment criteria for determining process capability.[10]

MAKING PERFECT PRODUCTS

Quality awareness can be raised and quality stabilized by introducing and promoting QC.

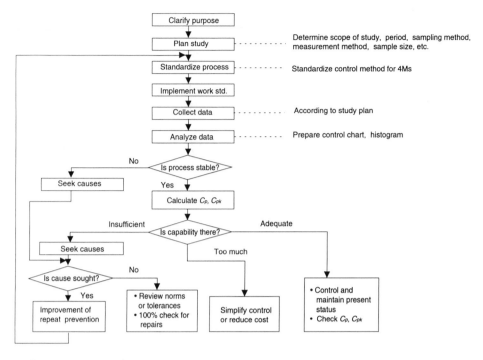

FIGURE 13.1. Procedure for process capability study.

- Market competition keeps getting tougher, and problems with the quality demanded by users are getting more severe.
- Product life cycles are getting shorter.
- Resources and energy must be conserved.
- Automation and process generalization are required.
- Nonzero rejection rates are persistent and are not being reduced to zero.

Here, the production of perfect products is important. ''Perfect products'' means those with zero defects and zero complaints, which is really quite difficult to realize. So we take this phrase as meaning ''products with near-zero complaints or defects.''

We may also call this ''ppm control''—ppm means parts per million. This unit is used, for example, for concentrations of minute amounts of sulfur oxides (SO_x) in the atmosphere, and ppm control is also used in reducing rejection rates for electronics or automotive parts, aiming at one part rejected per one million produced (0.0001%). The process capability study tells whether a product is perfect or not. The product must satisfy these two conditions:

TABLE 13.1. Calculation of process capability index (C_p, C_{pk}).

(ex.) Mean $\bar{x} = 50$; Standard Deviation $s = 0.48$

Upper Limit $S_U = 52$; Lower Limit $S_L = 49$

Classification		Distribution & Specs.	Formula	Example
Spec. on One Sides	Trend needs not be considered		$C_p = \dfrac{S_U - S_L}{6s}$	$C_p = \dfrac{52-49}{6\times0.48} = \dfrac{3}{2.88} = 1.04$
	Trend is to be considered	Center of specs.	$K = \dfrac{\mid (S_U + S_L)/2 - \bar{x} \mid}{(S_U - S_L)/2}$ $C_{pk} = (1-K)\dfrac{S_U - S_L}{6s}$ If $K \geq 1$, then $C_{pk} = 0$	$K = \dfrac{\mid (52+49)/2 - 50 \mid}{(52-49)/2} = 0.33$ $C_{pk} = (1-0.33)\dfrac{52-49}{6\times0.48} = 0.70$
Spec. on Both Sides	Upper limit (S_U)		$C_p = \dfrac{S_U - \bar{x}}{3s}$ If $\bar{x} \geq S_U$, then $C_p = 0$	$C_p = \dfrac{52-50}{3\times0.48} = 1.39$
	Lower limit (S_L)		$C_p = \dfrac{\bar{x} - S_L}{3s}$ If $\bar{x} < S_L$, then $C_p = 0$	$C_p = \dfrac{50-49}{3\times0.48} = 0.69$

C_p: process capability index; C_{pk}: that with trend considered.
K: degree of trend. | |: absolute value.

TABLE 13.2. Interpretation of process capability.

C_p (or C_{pk})	Distribution & Spec.	Evaluation	Action
$C_p \geq 1.67$	S_L S_U s $\overline{X}$	Too much capability	No concern of variation in products increases. Consider simplification of process or cost reduction
$1.67 > C_p \geq 1.33$	S_L S_U s $\overline{X}$	Sufficient capability	Ideal condition, maintain it
$1.33 > C_p \geq 1.00$	S_L S_U s $\overline{X}$	So-so capability	Run process control in a firm manner; when C_p nears 1, rejects can occur
$1.00 > C_p \geq 0.67$	S_L S_U s $\overline{X}$	Insufficient capability	Rejects are occurring, 100% check, control and improvement of process needed
$0.67 > C_p$	S_L S_U s $\overline{X}$	Capability very much insufficient	Quality is not satisfactory, improvement is urgently needed; review spec, too.

1. Not being out of specifications.
2. The process is stable, as shown in Figure 13.2.

To achieve perfect products, the quality characteristics of the products need to be watched carefully. Variation needs to be kept to a minimum in order to satisfy the customers. Some points to be considered in producing perfect products are as follows.

10 Points for Perfect Products

1. Set a level of perfection for rejects and complaints.
2. Understand the relationship between required quality characteristics and required process control features, in order to improve process capability.

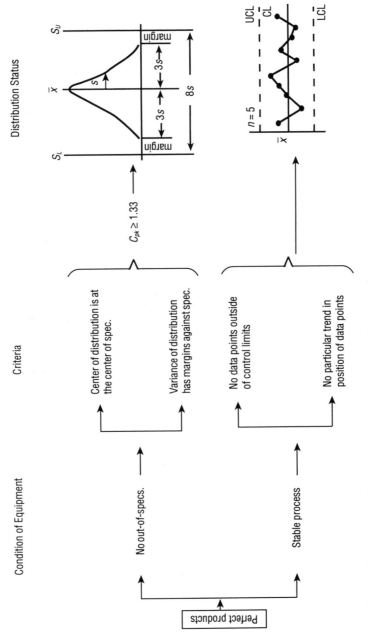

FIGURE 13.2. Statistical characteristics of a perfect product.

134

3. Perform work according to the steps for new product development, without skipping any of them.

4. Use FMEA and FTA to forecast problems and to solve promptly any quality problems that are discovered.

5. Improve engineering and work standards and comply with them.

6. Devise foolproof methods to prevent anomalies.

7. Enhance quality checks on initial, intermediate, and finished stages of the products.

8. Find a mechanism to discover rejects and develop equipment with a high capability index that will give a minimum of trouble.

9. Improve daily checks and maintenance control with equipment and tools.

10. Perform a thorough analysis of product defects to bring them up to a controllable level using a control chart.

CASE STUDY—PROCESS CAPABILITY IMPROVEMENT USING QUALITY PROCESS CHARTS

Introduction

Tokai Rika Co., Ltd. produces a variety of switches, seat belts, key cylinders, steering wheel locks, and other products. These are mainly automotive parts, and its Otowa plant produces key locks and cylinders for steering wheels. The steering wheel lock is a safety item with a complex mechanism. Thus, conventional control items and control methods were inadequate to maintain a quality that matched the design quality. A quality process (QP) chart using FTA to predict failure modes was prepared to select critical quality features and to maintain process capability. An example is introduced here (based on the account of M. Fukuoka, QC section, Otowa plant, Tokai Rika).[2d]

Outline of the Product

Figure 13.3 illustrates the product. The steering wheel lock is used with a key cylinder and locks the steering wheel to prevent the car from being stolen. At the same time, it also functions to open or close the electrical circuit to the starter motor.

Why the QP Chart Was Used

Figure 13.4 shows the QP chart used by this company, where the predicted failure mode is systematically broken down for deployment through part

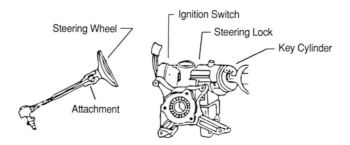

FIGURE 13.3.   Steering-wheel lock.

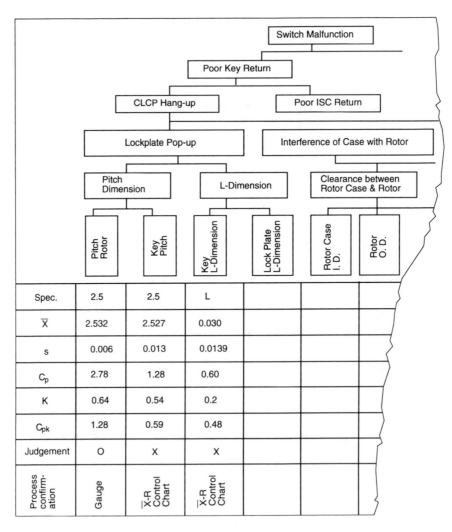

Process confirmation		Switch Malfunction					

	Pitch Rotor	Key Pitch	Key L-Dimension	Lock Plate L-Dimension	Rotor Case I. D.	Rotor O. D.
Spec.	2.5	2.5	L			
$\overline{X}$	2.532	2.527	0.030			
s	0.006	0.013	0.0139			
C_p	2.78	1.28	0.60			
K	0.64	0.54	0.2			
C_{pk}	1.28	0.59	0.48			
Judgement	O	X	X			
Process confirmation	Gauge	$\overline{X}$-R Control Chart	$\overline{X}$-R Control Chart			

FIGURE 13.4.   A QP chart.

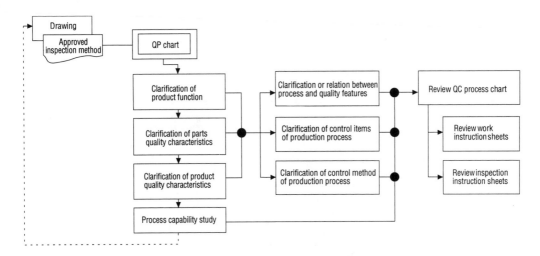

FIGURE 13.5. QP chart deployment.

characteristics and for integration into the control methods for the processes. Use of this QP chart had the following two purposes (see Figure 13.5).

1. Review the control method of the production process.
2. Clarify the status of process capability for the critical quality characteristics.

Effects of Using the QP Chart

There were two effects:

1. Characteristics with insufficient process capability were clarified and were subject to improvement.
2. Control characteristics were reduced from 141 to 28 as the control characteristics were further clarified. (See Table 13.3.)

Specific examples of these effects are given below.

TABLE 13.3. Clarification of control characteristics.

	Number of characteristics	
	Pre-improvement	*Post-improvement*
Parts	89	18
Subassemblies	48	6
Assemblies	4	4
Total	141	28

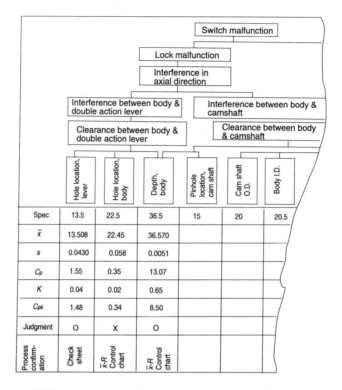

	Hole location, lever	Hole location, body	Depth, body	Pinhole location, cam shaft	Cam shaft O.D.	Body I.D.
Spec	13.5	22.5	36.5	15	20	20.5
$\bar{x}$	13.508	22.45	36.570			
s	0.0430	0.058	0.0051			
C_p	1.55	0.35	13.07			
K	0.04	0.02	0.65			
C_{pk}	1.48	0.34	8.50			
Judgment	O	X	O			
Process confirmation	Check sheet	$\bar{x}$-R Control chart	$\bar{x}$-R Control chart			

FIGURE 13.6.   QP chart deployment for lock malfunction.

Improving Design Tolerance

A part of the QP chart was deployed for malfunction of the lock, which is a failure mode of a steering wheel lock. This is shown in Figure 13.6. Figure 13.6 shows that the clearance between the double-action lever and the body, which was not specified in the drawing, was in fact a critical quality characteristic. (See Figure 13.7.)

1. *Process capability study on clearance.* This was studied for A (body depth), B (body hole 1), and C (double-action lever hole 1). The result was a C_p of 1.40, as shown in Figure 13.8. However, the parts process capability regarding clearance was sufficient for A and C but not for B, due to the equipment and other factors.
   - B is machined by a boring machine after casting, but improving accuracy was not economical.
   - A is determined by the die casting, and the present level of accuracy can be maintained.

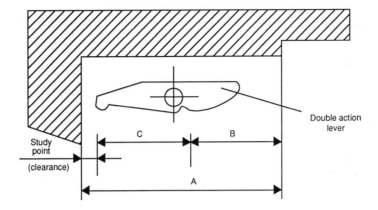

FIGURE 13.7. Clearance between lever and body.

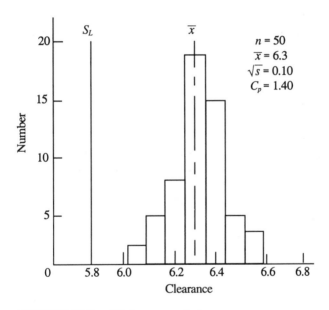

FIGURE 13.8. Histogram of clearance.

TABLE 13.4. Change in size tolerance.

Characteristic values	Pre-change	Post-change
Body depth	36.5 ± 0.2	36.5 ± 0.1
Location of body hole	22.5 ± 0.1	22.5 + 0.1 22.5 − 0.4
Location of double-action lever hole	13.5 ± 0.2	←

TABLE 13.5.   Process capability, pre- and post-tolerance change.

Characteristic values	Pre-change	Post-change
Body depth	8.50	1.96
Location of body hole	0.35	1.50
Location of double-action lever hole	1.48	←

Based on the above two points, resetting the values of the parts tolerance with consideration of the variance of the parts was judged to be sufficient.

2. *Setting the proper tolerance.* Since the body-depth clearance was already assured, the tolerances for A and B were reset by using the additive property of tolerances. The result is shown in Table 13.4. The result of confirming the process capability for the A and B dimensions, based on their reset tolerances, has assured a proper capability, as shown in Table 13.5. These results were fed back to the engineering department for design changes and review of the work standards.

Improvement of Process Capability for Key Cutting

The QP chart in Figure 13.4 shows the L-dimension of the key to be a critical quality characteristic, but because of insufficient process capability, as shown in Figure 13.9, the improvement described below was initiated.

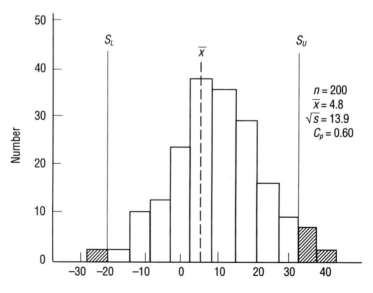

FIGURE 13.9.   Histogram of key L-dimension.

1. *Outline of process.* Figure 13.10 shows the cutting line of the key machine and the key configuration. The blank is pressed, a groove is cut, the L-dimension is cut, and it is plated and assembled.

2. *Process of analysis.* The factors for the L-dimension variation were pulled out from the cause-and-effect diagram in Figure 13.11 for the following analysis.
   - Variation in groove size
   - Wrong measurement of L-dimension

3. *Analyzing the groove cutting.* Figure 13.12 shows the results of a check of the relationship between groove size and L-dimension. The following points were considered.
   - Accuracy of the attachment tool for the groove-cutting machine. There are 28 attachment tools and their accuracy was checked with an $\bar{x}$–R control chart. The result is shown in Figure 13.13. This figure shows the different average values for the different tools. This value affects groove size. The result led to correcting the attachment-tool size and revising the tooling drawing.
   - Improved size cutting. Figure 13.14 is the result of an $\bar{x}$–R control chart check of the machine capability using one attachment tool for the groove cutter. The figure shows an insufficient machine capability. A precision check of this groove cutter showed where the problem lay, namely, in the bearing portion of the cutter, which had not been given as a check item. The addition of this check item for the bearing part and the specification for the groove size as a control characteristic were done to control groove size cutting.

4. *Analyzing the L-dimension measurement error.* The large effect on the key cylinder operation of the L-dimension means that high accuracy is

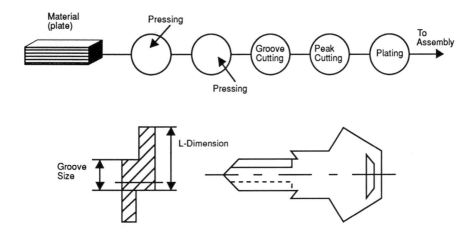

FIGURE 13.10.   Outline of key cutting.

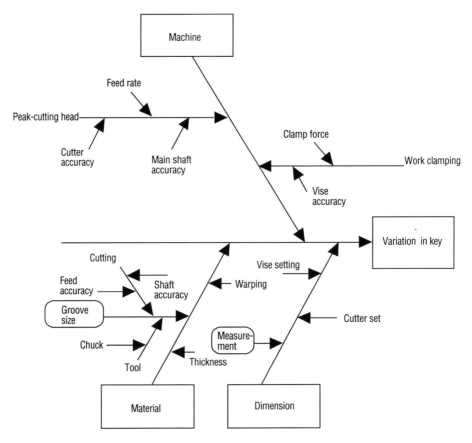

FIGURE 13.11.　Cause-and-effect diagram for key L-dimension.

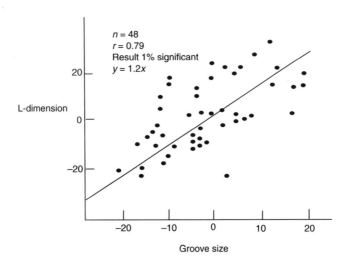

FIGURE 13.12.　Scatter diagram of key L-dimension
and groove size.

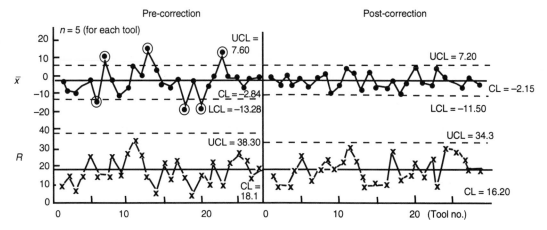

FIGURE 13.13.   Control chart for attachment tools.

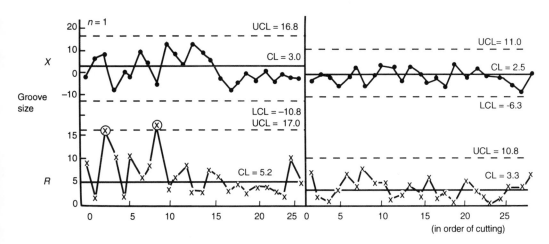

FIGURE 13.14.   Study of groove size cutting capability.

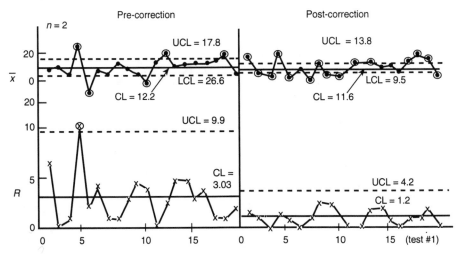

FIGURE 13.15.   Control charts for L-dimension measurement error.

143

necessary, and its measurement is difficult because of the complex shape. The measurement error was analyzed with an $\bar{x}$-R control chart. Figure 13.15 gives the results of this analysis and shows insufficient accuracy in measuring the L-dimension. An improvement was made by developing a new instrument and introducing automated equipment.

Summary of the Corrective Actions and the Results

The result of the above corrections was reduced L-dimension variation, as shown in Figure 13.16.

The following effects were also gained.

- L-dimension was made stable and the process capability was improved. (See Figure 13.17)

- The relationship between the L-dimension and other factors was clarified.

Standardization

This proceeded as follows.

1. Change the groove cutter specification.

2. Revise the check manual for the groove cutter.

3. Establish an L-dimension automatic measurement manual.

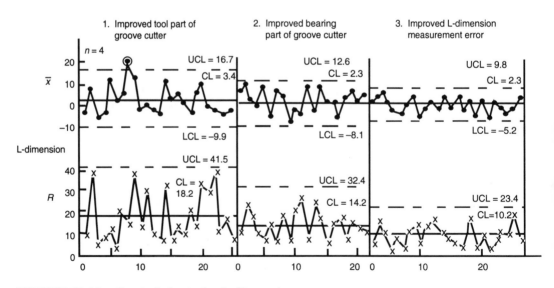

FIGURE 13.16.   Control charts for L-dimension.

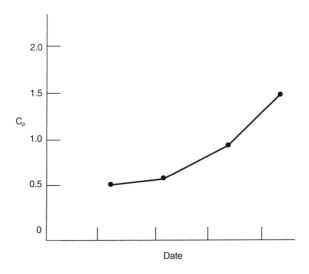

FIGURE 13.17. **Change in L-dimension process capability.**

In Conclusion

By using a QP chart, the control points and items for production processes were clarified. Improvement of the processes is often emphasized for maintenance of process capability, but a review of the tolerances provided the proper process capability here, and QP-chart effect on process control was realized. The use of the QP chart on other products should be emphasized.

14

Preventing Recurring and Potential Problems

—Do not make the same mistake twice. Prevent problems, both their recurrence and their happening in the first place.

THINK QC

The aim of quality control is to perform actions efficiently in production, sales, and service. Good products and services based on an understanding of the customers' requirements become consumer-oriented. The following actions are therefore necessary.

- Institute a consistent QA system throughout product planning, sales, and service in order to be able to offer products that are fitting for the market and of good quality.

- Improve the initial setup by thinking about the way the work is to be done. This will improve the company's organizational structure, resulting in continuous improvement.

- Use QC techniques positively, together with the specific technologies, in order to exert effective control and bring about improvement.

The level of QA can be judged as in Table 14.1.

As shown in Table 14.1, the quality assurance of a company's products and services needs the QC way of thinking. What is this QC way of thinking? It means using QC techniques based on a QC point of view and attitude in order to prevent problems from being repeated or from occurring in the first place. It means:

TABLE 14.1. Evaluation of level of QA.

Level	Criteria	DETAILS		Remarks
		Setup	Defects/misses	
Level 1	No QA setup	No written QA system and administration, implementation is in disarray	Many defects and misses	
Level 2	QA system in place	QA system and method of administration are there only in form	Persistent defects and misses	
Level 3	QA system is in operation	Written QA system and way of administration in form of 5W1H, trouble analysis is performed	Defects and misses are decreasing	QA system chart Complaint handling system chart 5W1H is: What—aim, target When—period Where—process, meeting, etc. Who—in-charge Why—reason How—methods
Level 4	No recurring trouble due to same cause	Smooth operation of systematic QA system trouble analysis	Steep decline in defects and misses	Trouble analysis sheets Standards Control data and their revisions
Level 5	Troubles are prevented beforehand	Problems are discovered beforehand, QA system is improved, upstream control of prevention	No trouble occurs	QA system chart Standards Control data Checklists FMEA FTA Quality function deployment Design review

- Detecting problems, looking for causes, and taking corrective actions to prevent their repetition.
- Predicting troubles at the planning stage, the design stage, and the trial production stage in order to prevent these potential problems from occurring, by the use of QC methods.

The aim of QC thinking is to raise the quality of the work by looking at the potential problems. It is necessary because:

- Troubles are usually handled only in a fire-fighting manner and they recur easily.
- Such problems are often passed on to later stages in production.
- Defects and mistakes are chronic and are not likely to decrease on their own.
- Only the process or the product having trouble at the moment is dealt with, and similar processes or products are ignored.
- The basic cause of the problem is not discovered, and corrective actions are not tied in with any improvement in work methods.

WHAT IS PREVENTION OF RECURRENCE?

One of the most basic responsibilities on the shop floor is maintaining a stable process which will produce quality that matches the targeted quality. A variety of preferred work methods need to be studied from a variety of angles in order to produce those products and services that will satisfy users. In addition, these studies should result in safe, rational, and high-efficiency work, as well as a high usage rate of materials and a high production rate. Problems can happen, however, even when a great deal of effort is spent in stabilizing the process. This is because of the workers being inattentive, the wrong materials being mixed, or the wrong work procedures being followed.

Problems may be actual or *predicted* harm or damage. Emergency actions are not enough, and it is necessary to prevent problems from being repeated. Unfortunately, many of the corrective actions taken by design, production, sales, and service departments are only emergency treatments. Attempts to prevent repetition of problems are rare.

Some examples are:

- Guests of a hotel complain that no towels are in their rooms. So towels are brought, but there is no effort to prevent this from recurring.

- Slow sales result in increased inventories which must then be sold at 40 percent discount. The same will happen again, unless reasons for slow sales are addressed.

- A complaint about superficial damage to a product occurs. So the item is replaced with another one immediately. Again, the cause of the damage or delivery of damaged goods to the customer needs to be looked into.

The cause of the trouble must be analyzed so that proper action may be taken to prevent recurrence of the problem.

The following three measures may be taken (see Figure 14.1).

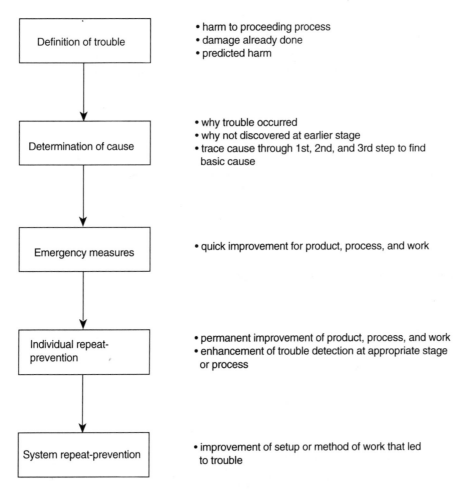

FIGURE 14.1. Set-up to prevent repetition of problems.

Measures to Prevent Repetition

1. *Emergency measures*—Patchwork-type actions for trouble that has already occurred. For example, change crimping, change adjustment.

2. *Efforts to prevent repetition for this individual item (permanent fix)*—A permanent measure for this particular product, process, or work problem. For example, correct a metal die, change a wall thickness, change material.

3. *Prevent repetition in the system*—Measures for systems, such as the way work is done, setup procedures, etc. to prevent trouble that originates in the same cause (procedure, engineering standard, control standard, organization, process) from recurring. For example, revising a QA system chart, adding critical control items (e.g., tensile strength, hardness), revising an engineering standard (e.g., test items).

Asahi Lighting Co. is located in Higashi Osaka City, which is near the city of Osaka. It is developing and producing light fixtures for homes together with Matsushita Electric Works. Their motto is to improve the pleasantness of life through better lighting.

This company uses a quality trouble analysis sheet, which is shown in Figure 14.2, for a systematic identification of causes and for taking corrective actions for items in the plant that have received major complaints from the marketplace. This sheet looks for causes on three levels to implement emergency, particular, and system problem repetition-prevention measures.

As a result, chronic reject or quality problems have decreased. A variety of in-house standards were improved and both tangible and intangible benefits were gained.

PREVENTING POTENTIAL PROBLEMS

As technology changes—and this is occurring more quickly these days—new products and model changes are needed. Otherwise, market share or profitability will suffer. But this quick pace of product change means that the life cycle of the product is getting shorter. Furthermore, improved machinery, energy conservation, cost reduction efforts, and faster production speeds can increase the number of problems, despite the considerable benefits.

We need to avoid:

- Troubles with critical products and loss of the customers' trust
- Delays in sales and poor timing
- Failure to achieve our target costs, resulting in loss of profit whenever we send a new product to the marketplace

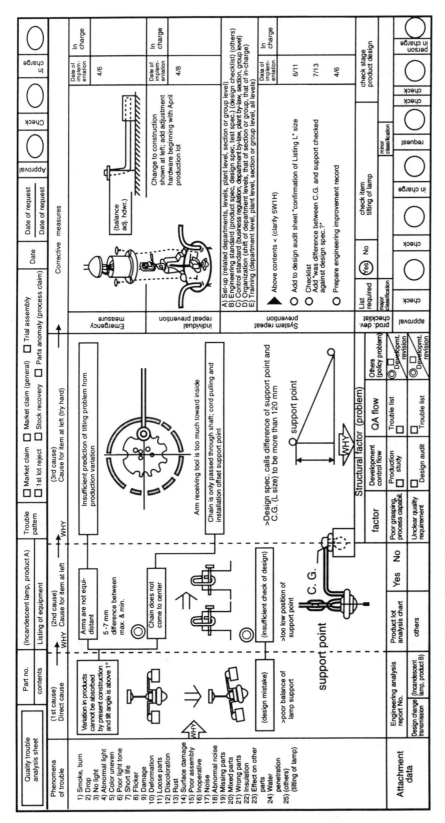

FIGURE 14.2. Quality-trouble analysis sheet.

151

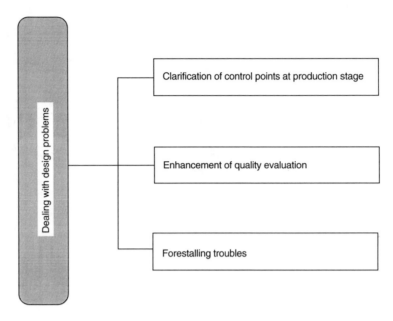

FIGURE 14.3.   Method of preventing potential troubles.

A sufficient amount of study, research, testing, production and sales data, planning, specifications, standards, and control data must be collected and examined to prevent troubles from occurring after production starts. The cost of this research at the prototype stage is much less than it would be after production has begun.

One of the basics of TQC is the concept of prevention. This is necessary in all control, and, needless to say, prevention is more economical than measures taken after the trouble has occurred.

The concept of prevention is also necessary for health and safety, for maintaining machinery and equipment, for studying the required quality, and for researching and developing scientific technology. TQC prevents potential problems from occurring.

Preventing potential problems means removing the causes by predicting the problems before they occur. To accomplish this, one needs to go back to the very source of the way the work is performed (upstream) to systematically seek first-, second-, and third-order causes for problems. The following points are necessary for preventing these problems. (See Figure 14.3.)

Points for Preventing Potential Problems

1. *Seek out problem areas in the design.* At the product planning stages, quality deployment is done to establish target quality based on the

demands of the customers. At the product design stage you can predict the potential problems and take preventive actions. The methods described below are very effective.

- *Quality deployment*—This expresses the relationship between required quality and the quality characteristics or quality elements, applying function deployment to the quality function. It is also called a quality chart, quality deployment chart, quality relation chart, required quality deployment chart, and by other names (see Figure 14.4).
- *FMEA (failure mode and effects analysis)*—This is a technique to analyze failure modes and effects in order to discover latent defects or incompleteness in the design (see Figure 14.5). FMEA is particularly useful for ranking the criticality of effects.
- *FTA (fault tree analysis)*—This is a technique for analyzing the paths and probabilities of chains of causes of problems by deploying them in a linear graph (fault tree, see below) to identify those items that need correction in order to assure reliability and safety.
- *FT (fault tree)*—This chart shows the relations between system faults and downstream phenomena in a logical pattern, using symbols for *and* and *or* (see Figure 14.6).
- *Design review*—This involves an audit and improvement of the product at the design stage, taking into consideration performance, function, reliability, cost, and delivery. People from the design, production, inspection, and operation departments participate in the audit.

2. *Clarify control points for the production stage*. To realize the design quality, control points for the processes need to be clarified, as follows.
   - What characteristics are to be controlled?
   - What parts or materials need to be controlled?
   - What is to be checked for these?

   In addition to the above, process FMEA and quality deployment are helpful.

   - *QA system chart*—Establish the QA process by dividing it into steps such as planning, design, production, service, and other items (functions); the departments in charge; and the data controlled (output). Standards for QA at each step can then be systematized in a chart (see Figure 14.7).
   - *QC process chart*—Processes from the raw materials supplies through shipment of the final product need to be charted, and the who, what, when, where, why, and how of the control of these processes need to be established. In other words, clarify the control items and the control method for each process (see Figure 14.8).

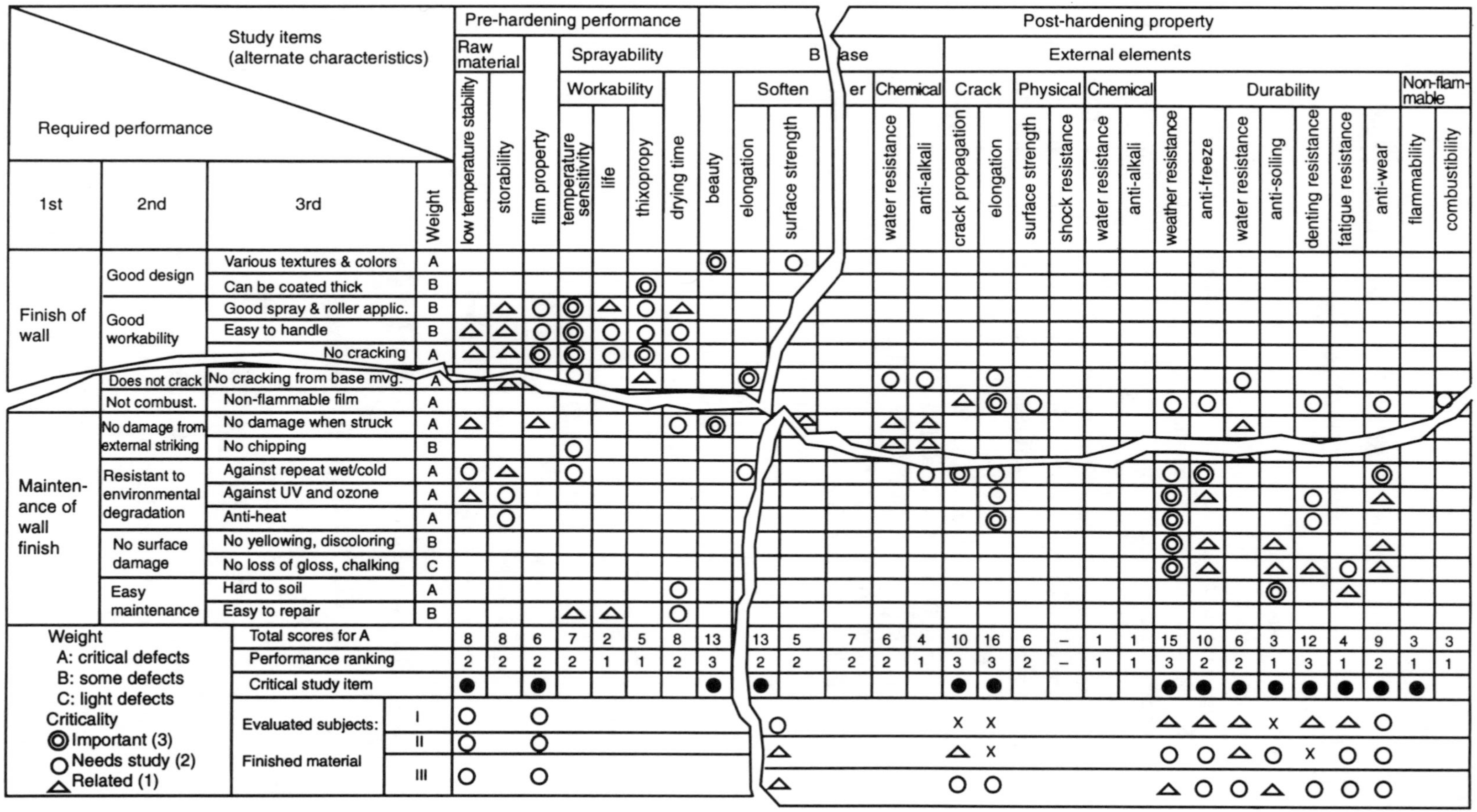

FIGURE 14.4. Required-quality deployment chart for spray-coated material.

Quality characteristics (column headers):

Pre-hardening performance
- Raw material: low temperature stability, storability
- film property
- Workability / Sprayability: temperature sensitivity, life, thixotropy, drying time
- beauty

Post-hardening property
- Base (Softer): elongation, surface strength
- Base Chemical: water resistance, anti-alkali
- Crack: crack propagation, elongation
- Physical: shock resistance, surface strength
- Chemical: water resistance, anti-alkali
- External elements / Durability: weather resistance, anti-freeze, water resistance, anti-soiling, denting resistance, fatigue resistance, anti-wear
- Non-flammable: flammability, combustibility

Required performance			Weight
1st	2nd	3rd	
Finish of wall	Good design	Various textures & colors	A
		Can be coated thick	B
	Good workability	Good spray & roller applic.	B
		Easy to handle	B
	Does not crack	No cracking	A
		No cracking from base mvg.	A
	Not combust.	Non-flammable film	A
	No damage from external striking	No damage when struck	A
		No chipping	B
	Resistant to environmental degradation	Against repeat wet/cold	A
		Against UV and ozone	A
		Anti-heat	A
Maintenance of wall finish	No surface damage	No yellowing, discoloring	B
		No loss of gloss, chalking	C
	Easy maintenance	Hard to soil	A
		Easy to repair	B

Weight
A: critical defects
B: some defects
C: light defects

Criticality
◎ Important (3)
○ Needs study (2)
△ Related (1)

Evaluated subjects: I, II, III
Finished material

154

Prepared: Nov. 1, 1984

Approval	In-charge
◯	◯

FMEA

System name (assembly name)	KB–218 Remo-Con.

NO.	Function block	Failure	Assumed cause	Effect of failure	Fre-quency	Criticality of effect	Detection ease	Danger priority	Corrective action	Remarks
	Remote control	Inoperative	• Variance in operation sensitivity. Contact resistance makes it inoperative	No remote control	Low	Medium	Hard	Low	• Wider range of contact resistance	
			• Faulty switching	=	Medium	Low	Easy	Low	• Use display device	
			• Poor CT small signal transmission. Detection voltage not generated for CT output	=	Low	Medium	Hard	Medium	• Use high micro core	
			• CT saturates under direct current (more often for 60 Hz)	=	Low	Medium	Hard	Medium	• Study saturation property of CT • Test contact resistance for wider range	
			• Detection amp saturates by induction	Wrong operation	Medium	Medium	Hard	Medium	• Separate CT for transformer reactor • Check effect of induction, well	
			• Waveform is warped, half-wave rectifier wave shows difference in positive/negative peaks for alternating current	Delayed operation time	Medium	Medium	Hard	Medium	• Check action of warped waveform at time of input	

FIGURE 14.5. FMEA of remote control unit.

155

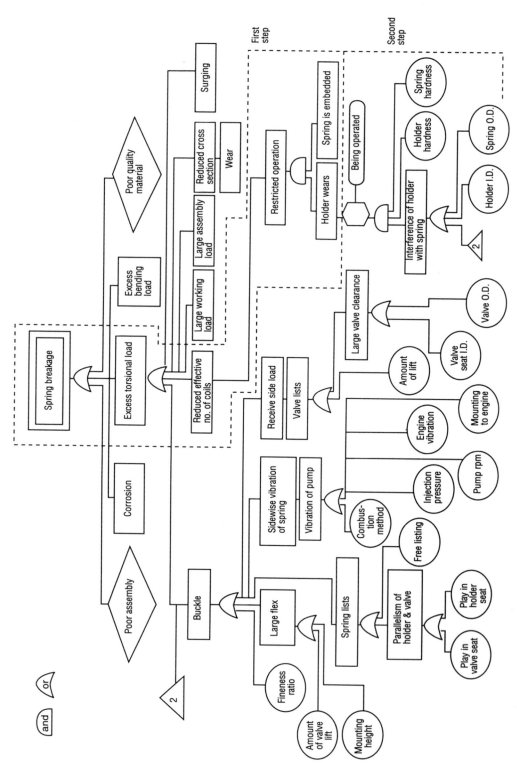

FIGURE 14.6. FT chart for valve spring of fuel injection pump.

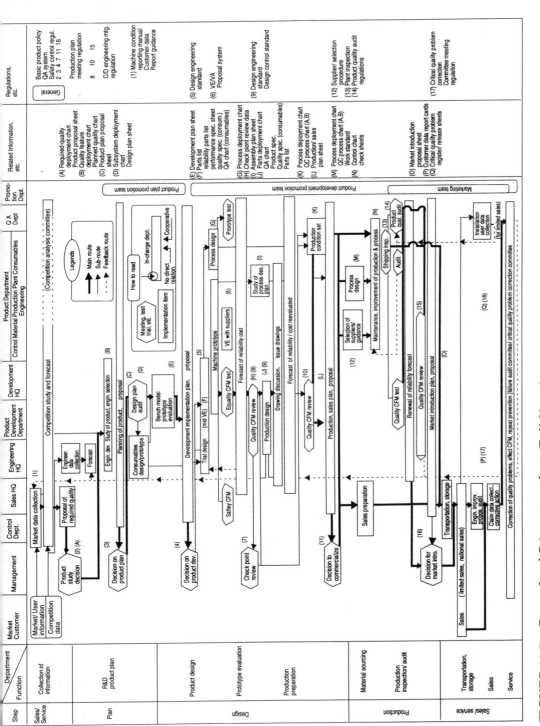

FIGURE 14.7. Example of QA system chart (Fuji-Xerox).

QC Process Chart
A-4 Concrete Work

Scope:
- Regular concrete, light concrete types 1 & 2
- Class of concrete, normal JIS standard
- Class of construction – 2, regular
- Concrete pump method
- Except hot/cold time work

Policy:
- CFM design criteria strength
- Concrete without cold joints
- Concrete with less cracks

	Issue	Approval
Issue	10/1/84	○ ○
Correction	10/20/84	○ ○
Correction		

Process step	Unit process	Control item	When	Frequency	Method	In-charge	Method	In-charge	Control record	Date In-charge	Standards	Remarks
					Control method			Treatment				
Preparation — Treat surface	Condition of surface	Free of dirt	Before work	All surfaces	Visual	In-charge	Re-clean	In-charge		In-charge		
Watering	Wetness of joints	Good & wet	Before work	All surfaces	Visual	In-charge	Water	In-charge		In-charge		
Receiving — Pump plumbing	Vibration prevention	Sufficient	After connection	End time	Visual	In-charge	Improve	In-charge		In-charge		
	Cement	Color, softness, etc.	At receiving	Each truck	Visual	In-charge		In-charge		In-charge		
	Designated clamp	In standard range >19 cm ±1.5 cm <18 c m ±2.5 cm	At receiving	AM & PM each 150 m3	Clamp test method (JISA 1101)	In-charge	Report to plant immediately for cause, return abnormal cement	Chief	Inspection result sheet	Chief	JISA 5308 JASS 5	
(Quality check at delivery of material)	Air amount	In standard range (regular cement) 3-5% (light cement) 4-6%	At receiving	AM & PM each 150 m3	Test of not-solid concrete (JISA 1128)	In-charge		Chief	Inspection result sheet	Chief	JISA 5308 JASS 5	
	(light concrete) Unit volume weight	In standard range ±3.5%	At receiving	AM & PM each 150 m3	Test of not-solid concrete (JISA 1116)	In-charge		Chief	Inspection result sheet	Chief	JASS 5	
	Amount of work per pump truck	<30 m3/h	During work	Once in AM & PM	Cement shipment invoice check	In-charge	Adjust delivery time	Chief	Work amount control sheet	Chief		

FIGURE 14.8. QC process chart for concrete work.

158

3. *Evaluating quality*. Quality evaluations must be performed to assure the quality going to the customers. These evaluations can be enhanced by dividing them into the following two types.

   • *Quality evaluation at the design stage*—Using past trouble data, engineering experience, and educated guessing you can detect defects and potential obstacles to achieving the target design quality, and therefore make improvements.

   • *Quality evaluation at the production stage*—The purpose of the first, second, and trial production prototypes is to confirm the target quality and cost of the item being produced. If sufficient quality is not exhibited at these stages, problems could crop up later. Thus, a process capability index (C_p, C_{pk}) is obtained using actual data from the trial production, and when problems are found improvements can immediately be made.

CASE STUDY—CREATING QC TOOLS THAT WILL PREVENT RECURRENCE OF DEVELOPMENT-STAGE COMPLAINTS

Matsushita Electric Works' lighting department develops, produces, and sells lighting fixtures and system products that use fluorescent lights and high-intensity discharge lights (HID) for public facilities. The market is somewhat glutted because of a decline in the amount of construction since the peak year of 1979. But the company is offering high-quality products based on the development of software and hardware technology for optimum lighting, so they are able to remain at the top of the market domestically.

This group introduced TQC in 1982 for the purpose of building a company organizational structure that would produce superior products that are number one in quality and based on "market-in" concepts. The TQC activities emphasized reducing problems by establishing a QA system that covers everything from the development stage to sales in order to prevent repetition of quality problems and to locate and prevent potential problems in a positive fashion.

The example in Figure 14.9 shows a method accumulating technology by preparing a product development checklist that uses personal computers to prevent problems from developing in the design stage of new-product development and in the preproduction stage. New check items can be added to the checklist based on past failures, so that the skill of any individual may be expanded to the highest level of the overall company skills, resulting in a reduction of development problems.

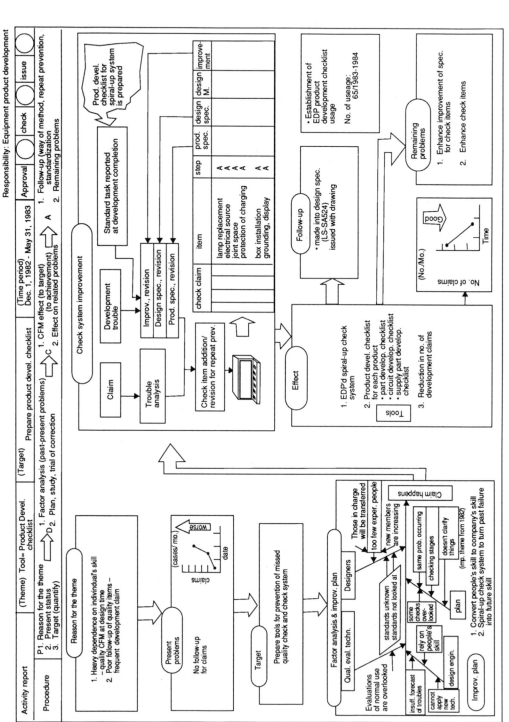

FIGURE 14.9. Computerized product-development checklist to prevent problems at design stage.

15

Upstream Control

—Control quality at the source, not downstream.

CONTROLLING AT THE SOURCE

In this period of slower sales and overstock, creating a demand among consumers by introducing new products is very desirable. Companies that are slow to respond to this need may lose their market share. For example, a camera manufacturer was slow to introduce a compact, lightweight camera. A sewing machine manufacturer missed out on the transition from mechanical to electronic systems. A personal-computer manufacturer was slow in introducing high-level-function, low-cost units. And a family-style restaurant did not continue to update its menu with appealing offerings, and so lost its youth business.

A positive type of quality control pushes for new products to create consumer enjoyment, as opposed to a passive quality control which merely protects the producers against rejects or defects. This positive QC is what we need now. To achieve it we need quality control at the source; that is, at the stages of product planning, design, preproduction, etc. Of course, such "upstream control" is necessary for the production of quality goods as well. It is far easier to prevent rejects from occurring in the first place than it is to deal with them later.

Thus, it is important to control quality at the planning and design stages rather than at the production stage, and this is necessary to avoid producing rejects. Controlling at the very source of the QA system is important. This upstream control for new market development, sales increases, and eliminating rejects is so important that it is now the emphasis in QC.

Upstream control means practicing control at the source by determining what product quality and service quality will be welcomed by customers, and going back to the source (upstream) where the work is initiated or where the purpose is first established.

In other words, we emphasize:

- What product is to be created in new-product development
- What technology is to be developed in new-technology development
- What troubles are to be anticipated in order to produce perfect commodities

The main points in upstream control are as follows.

7 Points for Upstream Control

1. Prepare or revise new-product development charts and QA system charts to develop a consistent system throughout, from the source to downstream.

2. Implement quality deployment. Clarify ''true quality'' from the viewpoint of the user and feed this into design quality and process control.

3. Emphasize the stages of development and match targets and actual results at each stage before moving on to the next stage.

4. Forecast troubles at each stage of planning, design, and preproduction trials to prevent downstream troubles from occurring later.

5. Initiate improvements at the development stages and carry them over into the whole setup.

6. Go after the causes of existing troubles, tracing them back to their very source, in order to enhance QA activities.

7. Prepare or improve various standards, specifications, flow charts, checklists, etc.

QUALITY FUNCTION DEPLOYMENT

The following two approaches exist for solving problems.

1. *Analytical approach*—To seek causes from results; to reach upstream from downstream.

2. *Design approach*—To clarify the means to achieve the purposes; to clarify the relations between upstream and downstream; to develop a systematic deployment; to look downstream from upstream.

Method 1 is the one that is used in conventional QC. Market complaints or in-process rejects are the subjects for this method. It was adequate when the mainstream of QC was to produce goods from given design drawings or specifications. However, when quality control was needed to supply goods to match users' needs with the proper timing, the analytical approach was no longer sufficient and the design approach became necessary. The source stages of new-product development are the product planning, development, and design stages, and so product design must be performed by understanding the required quality (quality that can create a new demand), and convert that to design features along with considerations of cost, etc. Quality function deployment serves this purpose.

Deployment of quality and deployment of quality function have been combined under the name quality function deployment. These terms have been defined by Professor Akao (of Tamagawa University) et al. as follows.[2g]

*   *   *

Deployment of quality, or quality deployment, is a systematic deployment of the relationships among quality of subassemblies, quality of parts, and elements of the process, based on an understanding of the user's requirements, and the converting of these into characteristic values for the purpose of deciding upon a design quality for the product. Quality deployment makes use of the quality deployment chart, or quality chart. A quality deployment chart is a chart that systematizes the real quality characteristics the customers say they want and displays the relationship between these and the design characteristics by converting the users' requirements into "counterpart" or "substitute" characteristics for the quality design. A quality deployment chart is prepared, generally, by combining a required-quality deployment chart and a quality-characteristic deployment chart in a matrix.

A quality function chart is one that systematically deploys the details of the job functions and the work needed to generate this quality. In other words, it expresses quality control work in the form of a system of purposes by deploying quality functions.

*   *   *

HOW TO PERFORM QUALITY DEPLOYMENT

The usual procedure is as follows (see Figure 15.1).

How to Perform Quality Deployment

Step 1. *Deploy required quality.* Understand market data in order to deploy the users' requirements for what needs to be produced, and pre-

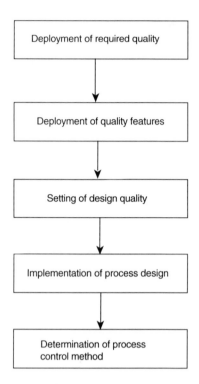

FIGURE 15.1.   Method of quality deployment.

pare a required-quality deployment chart. This is a systematic chart of the users' requirements as expressed in their own words. Generally, these are repeated from the upstream means to achieve these purposes through to the downstream steps, and can be expressed in a tree diagram or a system chart (one of the 7 New QC Tools).

Step 2. *Deploy quality characteristics.* Prepare a quality-characteristic deployment chart, which is a systematic chart of quality features. This is used to convert each downstream item deployed in the required-quality deployment chart into specific, measurable characteristics or values: the required-quality deployment chart and the quality-characteristic deployment chart are combined into a matrix (a two-dimensional chart) that displays the relationships between the individual items of one chart and those of the other.

Step 3. *Set design quality.* Once the requirements for and the characteristics of the final product are clarified, design quality is determined so as to achieve these and is then connected with specific technologies. By looking at the capabilities of existing technology, we can identify any need for what is called bottleneck technology, or technology to help us solve engineering bottlenecks.

At the next stage, function deployment charts, subassembly deployment charts, and parts deployment charts can be prepared as needed. A function deployment chart is a deployment of the product's functions into secondary and tertiary levels that deploys these functions in a scheme of purpose → means = purpose → means (see Figure 15.2).[11] Subassembly deployment charts and parts deployment charts are deployments into tree form of the relationship between the final product and the parts and subassemblies. They are particularly useful when the assembled product consists of many components and parts.[2g]

Quality evaluation items are then set by summarizing the various deployment charts to determine test methods. Implementation of FMEA, FTA, design review, etc. for quality improvement is also performed.

Step 4. *Performing process design.* Study the processes needed to integrate design quality into the process and to establish production methods. For example, here machining methods, equipment, metal dies and fixtures are deployed.

Step 5. *Determine the method of process control.* Prepare a process deployment chart to clarify the control features in order to enhance process control. A process deployment chart is a deployment of the users' required quality into characteristic values of the control characteristics of the processes and sub-processes for each part. The results are fed into the QC process chart and the work standards.

CASE STUDY—USING UPSTREAM CONTROL DURING THE DEVELOPMENT OF A LARGE-VOLUME LOW-TEMPERATURE LPG TANK MADE OF PRESTRESSED CONCRETE

Kajima Corporation began its companywide QC activities in 1978 in order to enhance its QA system to better meet the needs of the times and of society. Here is an outline of its development of the design and work methods for large prestressed-concrete (PC) low-temperature tanks from Kajima Corporation design headquarters.[2h] It is introduced as an example of upstream control in new-product development.

A PC low-temperature tank is used to store liquefied petroleum gas (LPG); the construction is shown in Figure 15.3.

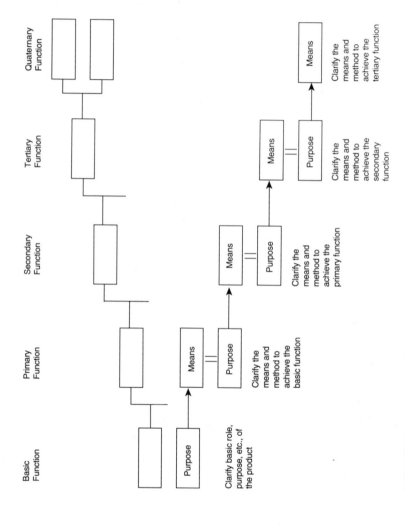

FIGURE 15.2. Tree diagram for function deployment.

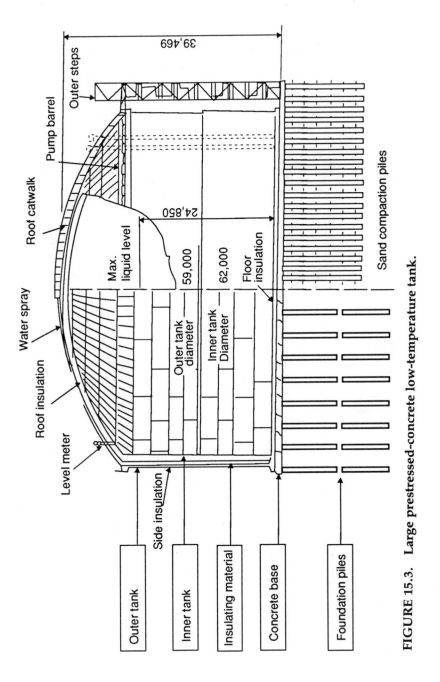

FIGURE 15.3. Large prestressed-concrete low-temperature tank.

167

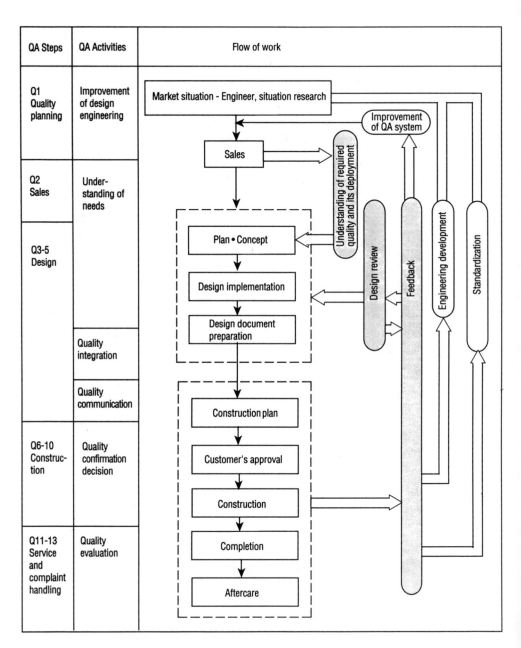

FIGURE 15.4.   Outline of QA system.

Background

With the oil crisis in 1974, LNG (liquefied natural gas) and LPG imports began increasing, and large low-temperature storage tanks that are both safe and economical were needed. The development of a new type of tank became necessary.

Establishing QA

The QA system in this company is outlined in Figure 15.4. Quality assurance is to be performed in a consistent flow from planning and design all the way through to service. The QA activities are implemented according to the system at each stage of the job.

Figure 15.5 shows the QA process when applied to this new type of PC low-temperature tank. The purpose of the process is to use upstream control to match the product to the customers' needs.

Implementing QA by Using Upstream Control

The process of upstream control as used at Kajima Corporation is best explained by describing each step along the QA process.

Step 1. Perform required-quality deployment to clarify customer needs at the same time as the new type of PC low-temperature tank is being developed (see Figure 15.6).

Step 2. A quality chart (1) was prepared for this task to clarify the quality features and criticality versus the required quality (see Figure 15.7).

Step 3. The engineering map in Figure 15.8 was prepared for development of the design-work engineering to see if the present technology of the company could match the work that was needed, and for selecting items to be deemed critical engineering development items. Furthermore, an FMEA was performed to evaluate predicted causes of failures that could affect the functioning of the tank. The results of this evaluation were included in the engineering map and were also considered in determining critical engineering development items (see Figure 15.9).

Step 4. QC techniques were used to implement the critical engineering development items, and adequate results were obtained. Table 15.1 shows the critical engineering development items and the QC techniques used.

Step 5. The items proven by the engineering development were fed back into the quality chart (1) for confirmation of counterpart charac-

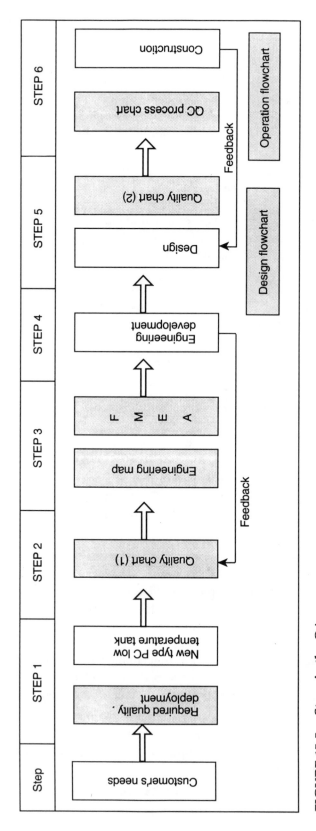

FIGURE 15.5. Steps in the QA process.

170

FIGURE 15.6. Required-quality deployment chart.

Basic	Primary	Secondary	Tertiary	Criticality	PC low temp.	Others A	Others B	Others C
Above ground low temperature tank	High degree of safety	Safety at leakage	Little gas spread	A	◎	△	◎	◎
			No outflow of liquid	A	◎	○	◎	◎
		Safety of tank external	No outflow of liquid	B	◎	○	○	◎
			Heat resistance for fire	C	◎	○	△	◎
			Strong low temperature shock strength	A	◎	△	△	◎
		Safety of ground base	Anti-earthquake strength	B	○	○	○	○
		Safe during earthquake		A	○	○	○	○
					◎		◎	◎
						○		
		General matls. are satisfactory		C	○		○	○
					○		○	○
	Economical	Effective use of land	Small area required	A	○	△	○	○
		No protection dike	No protection dike	A	◎	△	◎	△
		Low maintenance cost	No rust prevention	B	○	△	△	△
		Low construction cost	Low material cost	B	◎	◎	△	○
			Little equipment	C	○	○	○	○
		Low-cost operation	Low running cost of heater	B	△	○	○	△
			Low running cost of re-liquefying gas	C	○	○	○	○
Overall evaluation				Score	146	105	120	132
				Order	1	4	3	2

Legends:

Evaluation	◎	○	△
Criticality	A	B	C
Score	3	2	1

Calculation method of scores (ex.): criticality A and evaluation ○, score = 3 × 2 = 6

FIGURE 15.7 Quality chart (1)

Required quality	Quality features	Criticality	Top work	Foundation work	Shape	Seal, air below outer/inner tanks	Type of outer tank	D-1	Height of wall	Liquid depth at leakage	Type (Heater)	Temperature (Heater)	Standard concrete	PC steel	Steel girder	Steel/roof	Temperature insulator	Seal metal	Heat constant of concrete	Young's modulus of concrete	Young's modulus of PC steel	Heat constant of insulator	Young's modulus of steel	Concrete strength	Young's modulus of concrete	Material, PC steel	Young's modulus of PC steel	Steel girder	Own weight	Designed pressure	Roof load	Liquid pressure	Wind load	Wind load
		Crit.	A	A	B	A	A	A	A	B	A	A	A	A	A	A	A	A	A	B	B	A	B	A	B	A	B	A	B	B	B	A	A	B
High safety when liquid leaks	Small gas spread	A	◎		△		◎	◎	△					◎	◎		○	◎	△			○										◎	◎	
	No flow of liquid	A	◎				○										◎	○	◎	○	△	◎		◎	○	◎	△	◎				◎	◎	
	No combustion	A				◎																												
High safety at emergency	Heat resistance in fire	B	◎				◎						○		◎	△	○		◎	△		◎												
	High impact strength	C	◎				◎						◎	◎	◎	△		○	◎	△	○	◎	△										△	
	High low temp. check resis.	A	◎				◎										◎	○	◎	△		◎		◎	△	○	○	○						
High safety at normal time	Small residual sinking	B		◎																														
	Small unequal sinking	A		◎																														
	No surface sinking	B		◎																														
	Strong support	A		◎									◎	◎	◎	◎													○			○		
	Strong parts strength	A		△								◎	◎	◎	◎	◎	○	○	○	△	△	◎	△						○	○	○	◎	◎	
	No lifting by frosting	A	△								△	◎																						
High safety against earthquake	Sufficient quake resist.	A		◎													◎														△	○	○	○
	Small horizon mvmt.	B		◎																									△		△			
	Strong parts strength	A		△									◎	◎	◎	◎	○	○		△	△		△											
	No liquefact. of base	B		◎													○	○		△	△		△						○	○	○	○	○	○

Design

Required quality / Study item	Criticality	Loads	Loads combination	Material property normal temperature	Material property low temperature	Insulator	Thermal conduction	Temperature stress	Heater construction	Heater temperature	PC design	Circular building	Dynamics of upper work	Earth property	Sinking	Liquefaction	Soil improvement	Base piles	Base shrubs	Dynamics of base	Dynamic property
Group heads		Criteria				Method of study of low temperature stress					Upper structure			Design of foundation							Earth-quake resistance
Criticality		A	A	A	A	A	A	A	B	B	A	A	A	A	A	B	A	A	A	A	A
PC low temp. tank – High saftey – High safety against leakage	A	○	○		**○**	**○**	○	○													
No flow of liquid	A	**○**	**○**		**○**	**○**	○	**○**			**○**	**○**									
No risk of combustion	A	○		**○**																	
(unlabelled row)									○	○											
Strength of company's own technology – PC bridge – Design engineering		●	●	●							●		◐	○						○	○
PC bridge – Construction engineer.																					
PC water tank – Design engineering		●	●	●							●	●	●	●	●	●	●	●	●	◐	○
PC water tank – Construction engineer.																					
PC purge – Design engineering		●	●	●	○	○	◐	◐			●										
PC purge – Construction engineer.																					
LNG under-ground tank – Design engineering		●	●	●	○	◐	●	●	●	●		●		●	●	●	●		●	◐	○
LNG under-ground tank – Construction engineer.																					
Above ground tank foundation – Design engineering		●	◐	◐										●	●	●	●	○	●	●	
Above ground tank foundation – Construction engineer.																					
Degree of need for development		☆	☆	☆	★	★	☆	☆	☆	☆	☆	☆	☆	☆	☆	☆	☆	☆	☆	☆	★

Construction

Required quality / Study item	Criticality	Outer tank	Large PC	Outer / inner tanks	Bottom base	Heater	Insulation	Concrete work stress	Soil improvement	Piles	Base shrubs	Transportation of material
Group heads		Upper work							Foundation work			Other
Criticality		A	A	A	A	B	B	B	A	A	A	C
PC low temp. tank – High saftey – High safety against leakage	A			**○**								
No flow of liquid	A	○	**○**									
No risk of combustion	A											
Strength of company's own technology – PC bridge – Design engineering												
PC bridge – Construction engineer.		●	○	○	○					◐	◐	●
PC water tank – Design engineering								○				
PC water tank – Construction engineer.		●		○	◐				◐	●	●	●
PC purge – Design engineering								◐				
PC purge – Construction engineer.												●
LNG under-ground tank – Design engineering								●				
LNG under-ground tank – Construction engineer.					●	●	●		●	●	●	●
Above ground tank foundation – Design engineering												
Above ground tank foundation – Construction engineer.					●				●	●	●	●
Degree of need for development		☆	★	★	☆	☆	☆	☆	☆	☆	☆	☆

FIGURE 15.8. Engineering map.

Parts	Function	Failure mode	Effect of failure	Assumed cause	Criticality Frequency	Effect	Ease handlg	Evaluation	Grade	Remarks
Side wall	Previous flow-out of liquid at leakage	Crack generation	Gas leakage	Abnormal load to earthquake	1	4	4	16	A	Needs dynamic analysis, including base pilings
				Damage of pilings due to earthquake	1	4	4	16	A	
				Damage of base slab due to earthquake	1	4	4	16	A	Needs analysis of temperature stress
				Temp. stress due to low temp.	1	4	4	16	A	
				Poor concrete work	2	2	2	8	C	
				Poor PC steel work	2	2	2	8	C	
				Uneven sinking of piling	2	2	2	8	C	
				Lack of strength, steel, PC material	2	3	2	12	B	
				Poor quality of concrete	2	3	2	12	B	
		Excessive deformation	Breakage of insulation & seal metal	Low temperature stress	1	4	4	16	A	Needs analysis of temperature stress
				Earthquake load	1	4	4	16	A	Dynamic analysis including base piling
				Lack of cross section	2	3	2	12	B	
		Fracture of cross-section	Flow-out of liquid	Earthquake load	1	4	4	16	A	Dynamic analysis including base piling
				Damage of piling due to quake	1	4	4	16	A	
			Spread of gas	Low temperature stress	1	4	4	16	A	Needs analysis of temperature stress
				Poor concrete quality	2	3	2	12	B	

FIGURE 15.9. FMEA of low-temperature tank.

174

TABLE 15.1.   Critical engineering development items.

Critical engineering development items	*QC technique used*
1. Quake resistance of whole tank (improved dynamic property of soil base)	Regression analysis
2. Analysis of low-temperature stress (setting of design thermal conductivity)	Dispersion analysis
3. Setting of design criteria (setting of low-temperature material property)	Regression analysis
4. Construction method for inner-tank-related items	Correlation chart/system chart
5. Development of large PC construction method	Test/plan method

teristics. The design of the tank was based on this chart, and the setting of design conditions and design calculations, and preparation of the drawings, were performed according to the design flowchart in Figure 15.10. This resulted in a design that responded to the needs of the customer.

The quality chart (2) in Figure 15.11 was used to transmit the purpose of the design to the construction crews. Here, the quality features and quality chart (1) were compared with the construction process control characteristics in order to set specifications for on-site control.

Step 6. Control features transmitted by the quality chart (2) to the construction crews were reflected in the process chart for clarification of the "who, what, when, why, where, and how" of the construction work control (see Figure 15.12). Construction procedures went according to the work flowchart in Figure 15.13, and the inner and outer tanks were constructed simultaneously, resulting in a shorter work period. The completion occurred only 18 months after the start.

In Conclusion

A QA system with upstream control as explained above has given this company the following tangible and intangible benefits.

- Planning, design, work, and service were provided that matched the needs of the customers.

- The flow of the work was smooth, resulting in a reduction of waste and other hardships.

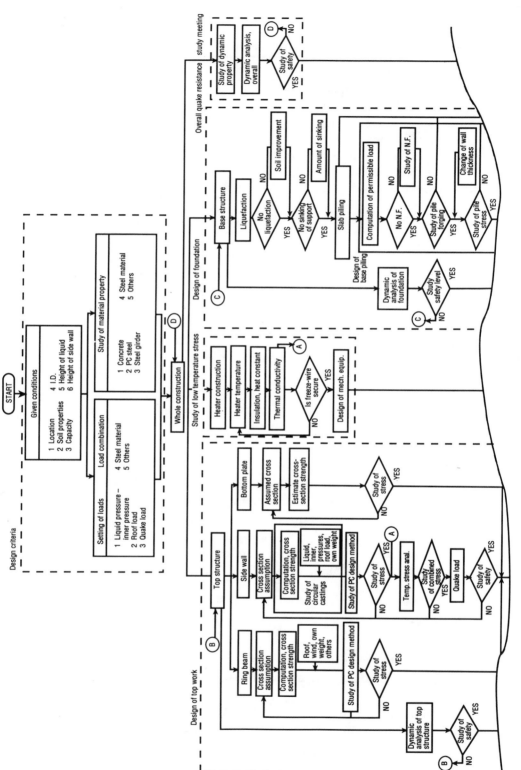

FIGURE 15.10. Design flowchart.

176

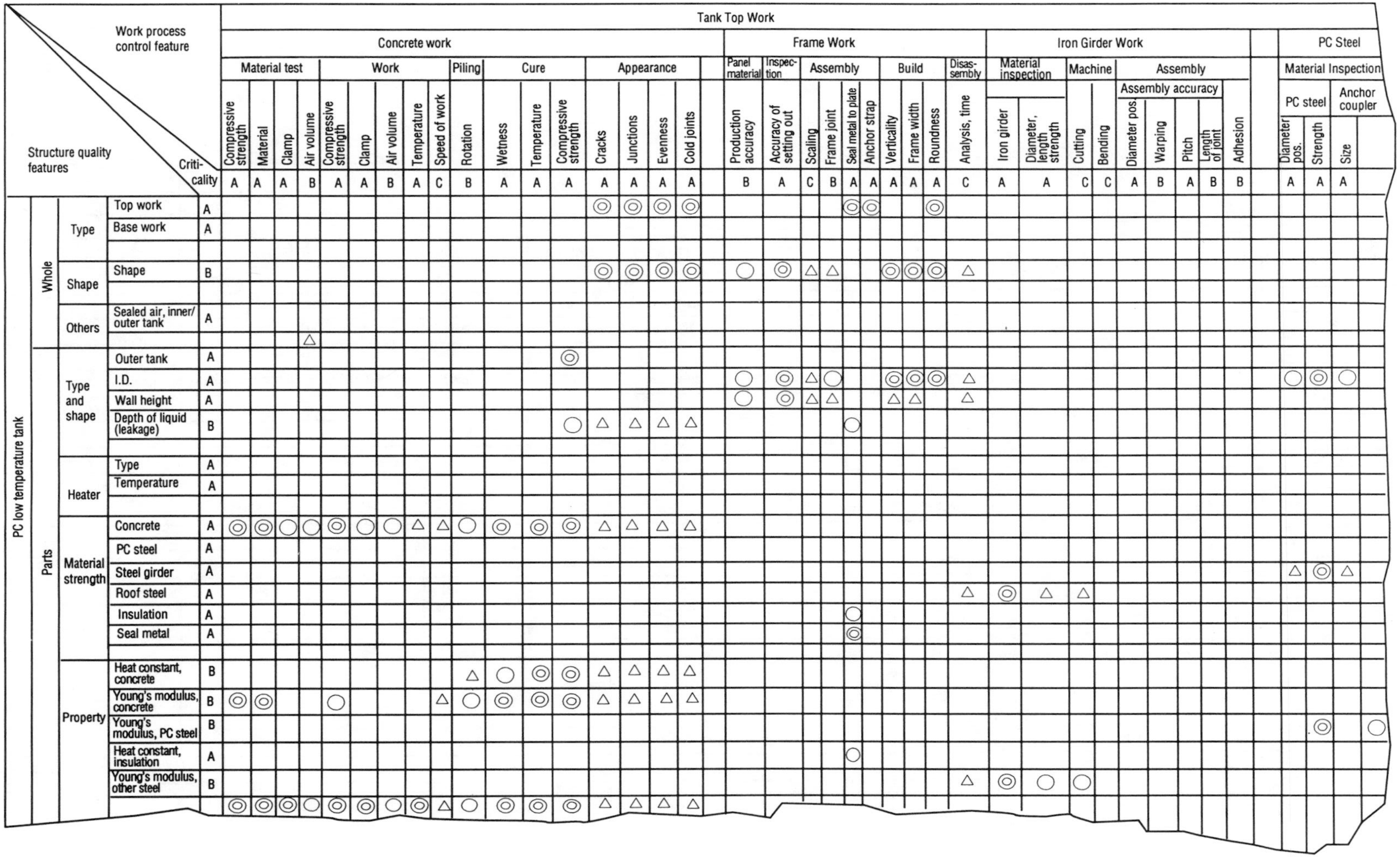

FIGURE 15.11. Quality chart (2).

Work office				(Revision)
Construction	LPG Tank (top work)			(Revision)
			Issue	Date
				Date

PC steel

Work procedure				Control item		Control method					Defect handling		Time period, stds.
Process	(criticality)	Type	Tools	Control point (check pt.)	Spec.	Check item	Freq.	Tools	Control in-charge	Record	In-charge	Method	
Material check	A	PC bars	—	(pcs shape)	Yes, no	Diameter length	rcvg.	Scale, visual	Material	Check sheet	Work chief	Change, replacement reorder	Ship paper, P.O.
	A		—	Strength, Young's modulus	JIS	thread, pcs	postrec.	Visual	Control chief	"	"	– – –	Mill sheet
	A	PC bar, twist wire	—	(pcs length)	Yes, no	Yield pt. elongation	rcvg.	"	Material	"	"	– – –	Ship paper, P.O.
	A			Strength, Young's modulus	Assoc. std.	Tensile	postrec.	"	Control chief	"	"	– – –	Mill sheet
	A	Anchor coupler	—	(shape, pcs)	Yes, no	Diameter length	rcvg.	"	Material	"	"	– – –	Ship paper, P.O.
	A			material	Good/bad	No. of drums	postrec.	Scale, visual	Control chief	"	"	– – –	Mill sheet
PC bar machining	B	Anchor mount	Welder/wrench	(slack)	Good/bad	Yield, elongation tens.	postwork	Visual	Worker A	Check sheet	Work chief	Repair	Assembly manual
	C	Sheath mount	Cutter	(length, joint)	"	Size, shape, pcs	"	Scale	"	"	"	"	"
PC bar assembly	A	Assembly accuracy	Crane hacker	location	< ±10 mm	Strength, quality	postwork	Scale, visual	Worker A	Control Rept.	Foreman	Repair	Drawing
	A		"	vertical	< ±15 mm	Unit, spiral-weld	"	"	"	"	"	"	"
	A		"	interval	< ±20 mm	Diameter length	"	"	"	"	"	"	"
	A		"	warp	< ±10 mm	Spaces, sheath to frame	"	"	"	"	"	"	
	A	Coupler joint	Pipewrench/turner	thread	50 mm	Sheath to frame	Lightness	When joined	Visual	Check sheet			
		Coupler / sheath joint		seal	Good/bad	Good/bad	Vinyl tape	"	"	"			
PC cable assembly	A	Sheath mount											
	A												

FIGURE 15.12. QC process chart.

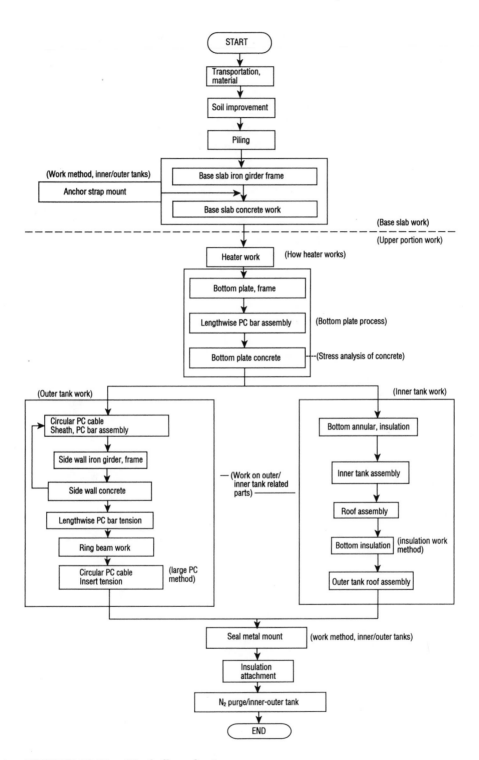

FIGURE 15.13.   Work flowchart.

- Deployment of an organized system of quality control resulted in record high-quality construction.
- Activation of the organization was achieved.

Finally, the introduction of TQC increased awareness about quality, and any remaining specific deployments of quality that have not been used so far will require further efforts and improvement.

16

Education

—Enhance education and training for development of human resources.

BASIC APPROACH TO EDUCATION

It is often said that QC starts with education and ends with education. In other words, education is important at the introduction of QC and for its promotion. Well-run QC education, both inside and outside a company, is one of the features of QC in Japan. Education aims at improving the knowledge, skills, and ethics necessary to sustain development of the company and developing human resources by understanding the ability and personality of each of the employees.

Education, including dissemination of information, is emphasized in the Deming Prize audit through the following check points.

1. The education plan and performance
2. Understanding of QC; quality awareness and control awareness
3. Education in statistical concepts and methods, and the level of penetration
4. Understanding the effects of education
5. Educating related companies (especially companies within the group, suppliers, outside contractors, and sales organizations)
6. QC circle activities
7. System and implementation of improvement suggestions

The basic concept of education at one of the Deming Prize recipient companies is described below (see Figures 16.1 through 16.3). Education needs to be advanced continuously using the following basic concepts.

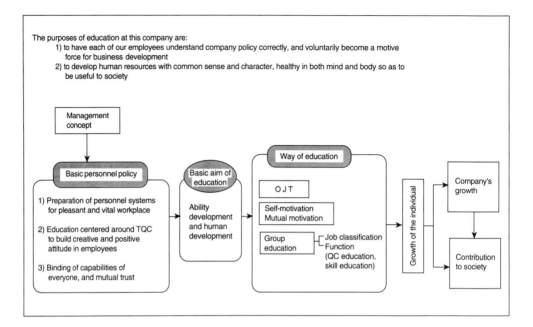

FIGURE 16.1.   Education at Kayaba Kogyo Co.[1d]

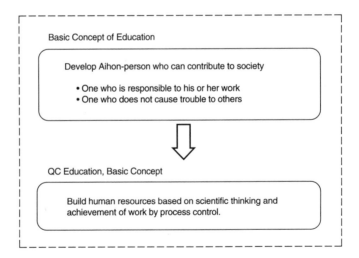

FIGURE 16.2.   Education at Aihon.[1c]

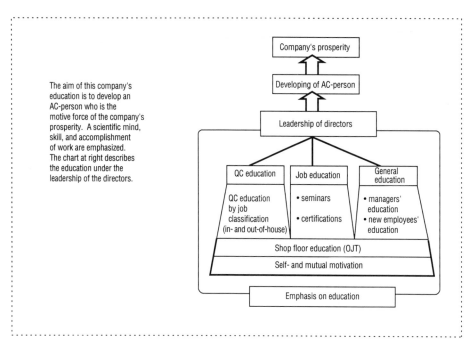

The aim of this company's education is to develop an AC-person who is the motive force of the company's prosperity. A scientific mind, skill, and accomplishment of work are emphasized. The chart at right describes the education under the leadership of the directors.

FIGURE 16.3.   Education at Aisin Chemical Co., Ltd.[1b]

1. Classify subjects and systematize courses for improvement in the level of employees.

2. Tie education in with people's normal activities in an organic way, providing positive opportunities and places for education.

3. Inculcate cooperation in the employees of the organization as well as in society, thereby enhancing the character and knowledge of the people, as is required of members of society.

To accomplish this, in-depth study and administration of education and personnel systems are necessary. This method of human resource development is shown in Figure 16.4.

EDUCATION SYSTEM

We need to place more weight on teaching capabilities than on merely transmitting knowledge, particularly when this is applied to work areas and when QC education is to be implemented.

Generally, QC education at companies is started by company policy or at the request of a work area, so this education needs to be appropriate to the company within its existing systems and to maintain continuity. QC educa-

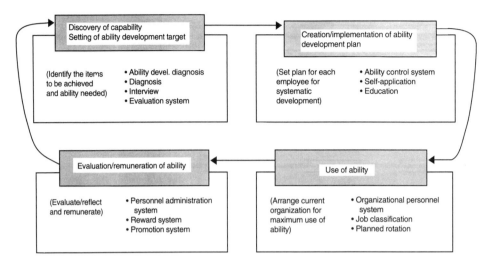

FIGURE 16.4. Human resource development.

tion should be systematized in terms of the company's development and its long-term expectations, just like any other specialty education.

The current status of the company, its future, the ability of the employees, and the method of education should all be well-studied to make the system work. In these cases the degree of understanding of QC, the status of QC circle activities, and TQC-promotion status also need to be considered. Figure 16.5 shows the education system at Toyota Motor Corporation's purchasing department (which is in charge of buying auto parts, raw materials such as steel, resins, plant machinery, and equipment). Figure 16.6 shows the education system at Yaskawa Electric Mfg. Co., Ltd.

QC EDUCATION

Method of QC Education

QC education can be done:

1. In-house
2. Outside the company

When done outside (seminars, etc.) the instructor is not always the same person, but the instructors may be people with a great deal of experience and knowledge of other company situations, so that students from a variety of companies can learn together. Thus, outside study should be combined with in-house study.

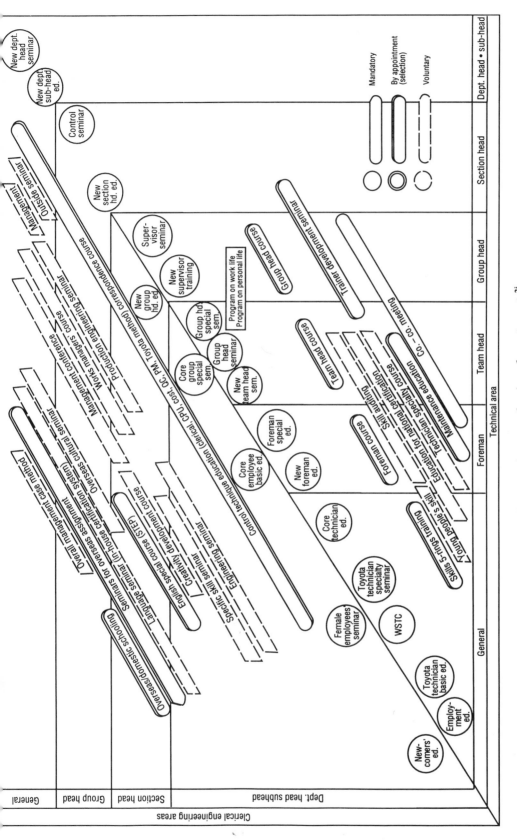

FIGURE 16.5. Education system of Toyota Motor Corporation purchasing department.[21]

FIGURE 16.6. Education system at Yaskawa Electric Mfg. Co., Ltd.[2j]

Job class	Quality Education (In-house)	Quality Education (Outside)	Sales job (In-house)	Sales job (Outside)	Functional education — Clerical job (In-house)	Functional education (Outside)	Branch office group education
Directors	Top seminar	QC special course / QC management special course					Study of specific items to each branch
Dept. Hds.	Dept. hd. sem.	QCC top course					
Sect. Hd.	Sect. hd. sem.	QCC/PTA course / TQC promotion course / QCC promotion course	Sales engineering instruction course			TQC instructions	Core eng. study / Engineer. study / Engineer. study
Group Heads	Group heads / Group hd. sem.	Group head seminar / TQC instr. course / TQC mgr. course / QCC school / PL course	Market research seminar		Software prod. control seminar		CPU lessons / English lessons
General	New QC seminar / TQC foreman course / Safety course / QC seminar Foreman basic course				Reliabil. case study / SQC case study	Spec. eng. outside crs. / Reliabil. case study	CPU study / Meeting plan study
General above 2 class / above 3 class	Core people seminar	QCC leader course / Repeat prevention course / New QC course / Brother seminar / OCC basic course / Purchasing QC course / Sales QC course / Variables analysis course / Functional control course / Youth boat / QCC sailing sem	Sales course / Sales special course / Sls. eng. crs. / Sales basic course		SQC case study / Reliability study / IE seminar / VE seminar / Dev. engin. seminar / Pat. engin. seminar / Dev. eng. seminar / Prod. eng. seminar / Service seminar / Creativity course		Fem. wkrs. sem. / Tech. intro. sem.
New employees	Follow-up study II / Introduction seminar / Education per class		Sales intro course				Follow-up study II / Female workers intro. sem.

Total company group education

In-house education includes:

1. Off-the-job training (OFFJT)
2. On-the-job training (OJT)

OFFJT means away from the shop floor, so it is suitable for a more systematic study of a particular subject. OJT is for teaching the knowledge, skills, and attitudes to perform the work and is usually taught by senior employees on the shop floor. It is more practical to do it this way.

One major feature of QC education is QC circle activity. This develops self-motivation or mutual motivation and is also very close to the activities on the shop floor.

Practical QC Education

The following three items are basic in QC education for all employees.

1. QC concepts (QC point of view and attitude)
2. QC work methods, QC implementation
3. Statistical thinking and data analysis methods (QC techniques)

The program for a course normally includes the following points, but the actual content of a course can vary depending on the subject.

General Points to Include in Course Programs

- Name of the course
- Aim or target
- Subjects and students
- Schedule
- Location
- Courses and contents (items ordered, texts, etc.)
- Instructor
- Texts used
- Tools (overhead projectors, video recorders)
- Emphasis
- Cautions
- Actual questions and answers
- Homework and answers
- Test problems and answers

- Study meeting items (aims, selection of themes, activities, reports, result reports, and presentation of results)
- Completion criteria
- Confirmation and evaluation of the results

Points for QC Education

The following points need to be attended to in QC education.

10 Hints for Successful QC Education

1. QC education holds a core position in total company education programs. Get rid of such ideas as "we don't need QC," or "TQC is separate from production," and put QC education within the overall education system together with TQC and tie it in with management education and training.

2. Education should start with senior job positions. Top management is the leader of TQC. Education must apply to top positions deeply related to TQC and then expand downward to lower positions.

3. Educate all employees at all job levels. To establish QC for good results, QC education must be for all. A common language must be applied for all QC concepts and QC techniques. Set a curriculum for each job level and cover all levels. Do not let some people get away with the excuse later on that they didn't know something because they did not receive a QC education.

4. Make sure the basic QC concepts are well understood. Make sure an understanding of "quality first," the PDCA cycle, priority orientation, management by facts, process control, consumer orientation, downstream processes as the customer, use of QC techniques and the other topics described in this book are well understood by everyone.

5. QC techniques are the key to solving problems on the shop floor. Use of QC techniques, particularly the 7 QC Tools, must be taught thoroughly with examples and with practice. The 7 QC Tools should be a mandatory course for all managers all the way through to the top.

6. Group discussion is a part of the curriculum. One-sided instruction is important, but group discussions must also be included. Practice is also essential for good comprehension. Group discussions make for better communication and a more open workplace.

7. Use examples from your own company. QC concepts and techniques are common in many types of work, but one's own examples are better for understanding. Expressions like, "Now I understand," "Hey, we can use it here," can come from such examples. Some

texts prepared by companies are okay, but if the descriptions are not well explained or if there are no good authors within a company, use commercial textbooks.

8. Use case study, technique study, and on-the-job training. Do not stop at knowledge, but look for practical uses as well. Meetings and practice need to be held and run regularly.

9. Follow up all education. QC education's purpose is not knowledge alone, but practice; and this requires follow-up. Make known your group's themes for better follow-up and for systematic quality improvement, efficiency improvement, and cost reduction based on the theories, techniques, and examples used at educational meetings.

10. Have a TQC promotion office or educational section administer the education program. TQC offices and education sections need to work closely together to administer QC education, as it is the core of total company programs.

EDUCATION AND COMMUNICATION ACTIVITIES AT TOKYO JUKI INDUSTRIAL CO., LTD.

Education activities at the industrial sewing machine department of Tokyo Juki Industrial Co., Ltd. are described below.[1c] This department is a leader in its area of developing new, automatic thread-cutting machines with mechano-electronic features in the field of industrial sewing machines. In 1981, it received the Deming Prize for its QC, policy control, QC circle activity, specific technologies, and QC techniques.

Aim of Education

Figure 16.7 shows the five aims of its education program.

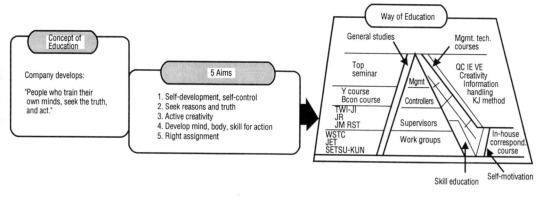

FIGURE 16.7.   Goals and means of education.

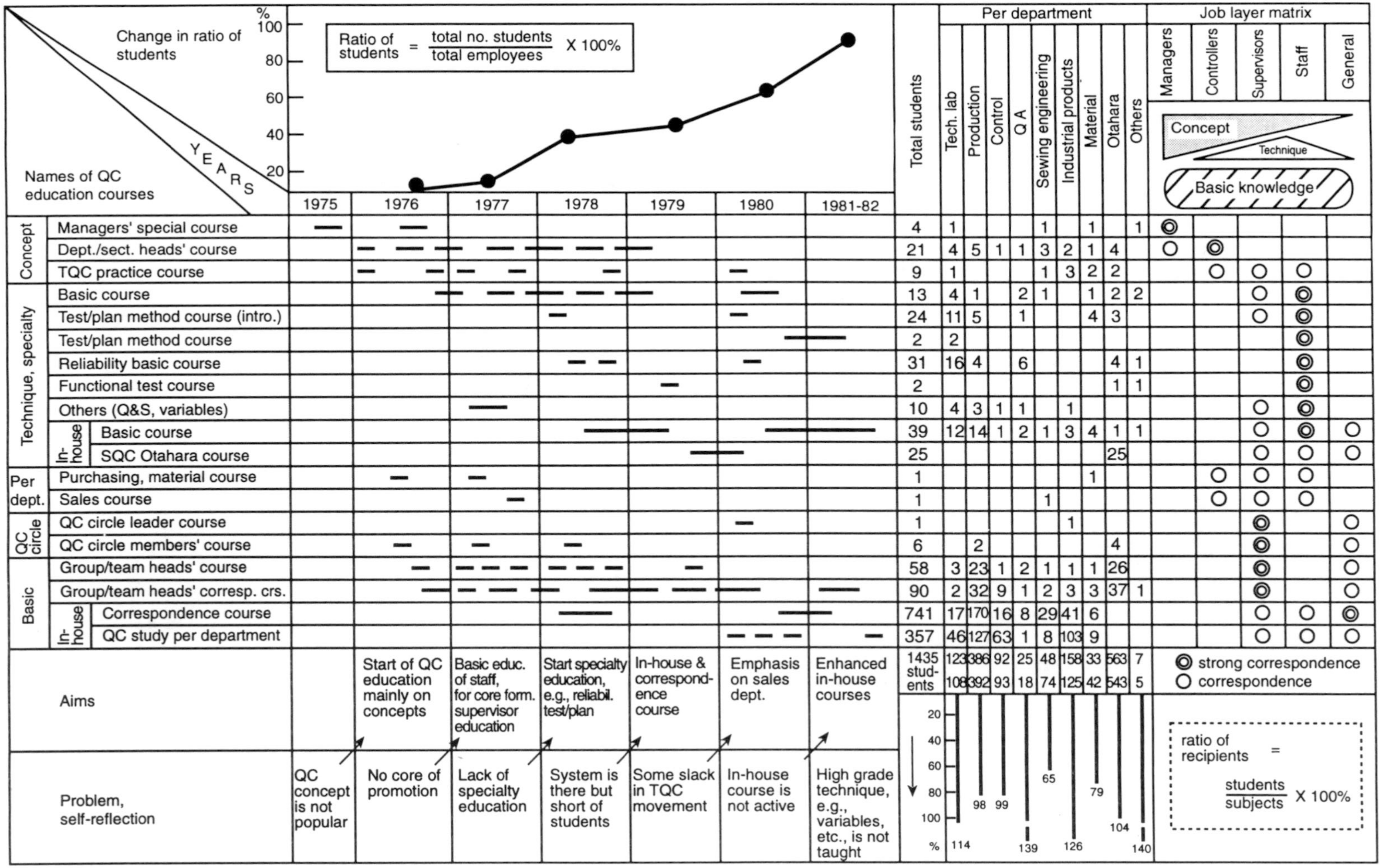

FIGURE 16.8. History of QC education and job-level matrix.

Implementation

- *QC education*. Figure 16.8 shows the history of the QC education system for each job level. Dissemination of the QC education began in 1976 and is evidenced by the number of applications of QC techniques shown in Figure 16.9. The in-house courses have trained in-house instructors in order to apply QC education more widely.

- *General education*. Given the companywide education policy that the company should invest in people who will develop their minds, seek truth, and act accordingly, this puts a great weight on the department of human resources. An in-house correspondence course was started in 1980 (see Figure 16.10).

- *Skilled technician seminar*. A system of certification of skills based on the 1964 Occupational Training Act was introduced to improve skills for higher quality, and it has produced many skilled technicians. A technicians' group was started in 1966 and was instrumental in promoting this work. Qualification tests were instituted, and certified workers received personnel consideration.

  Jobs subject to this qualification now exist in machining, finishing, sewing machine maintenance, drawing, drafting, etc. (refer to Figure 16.11).

Effects and Problems in Education

Effects	*Problems*
1. QC education systematizes the work of the controllers and the supervisors.	1. The "3 realities" (observe real things on the work floor) are not well established.
2. More people talk in terms of data.	2. Insufficient QC circle activities.

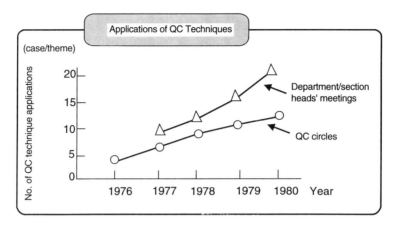

FIGURE 16.9.   Number of applications of QC techniques.

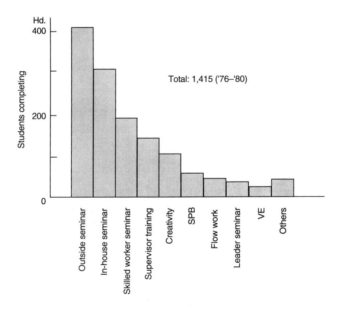

FIGURE 16.10.   Completions of general education.

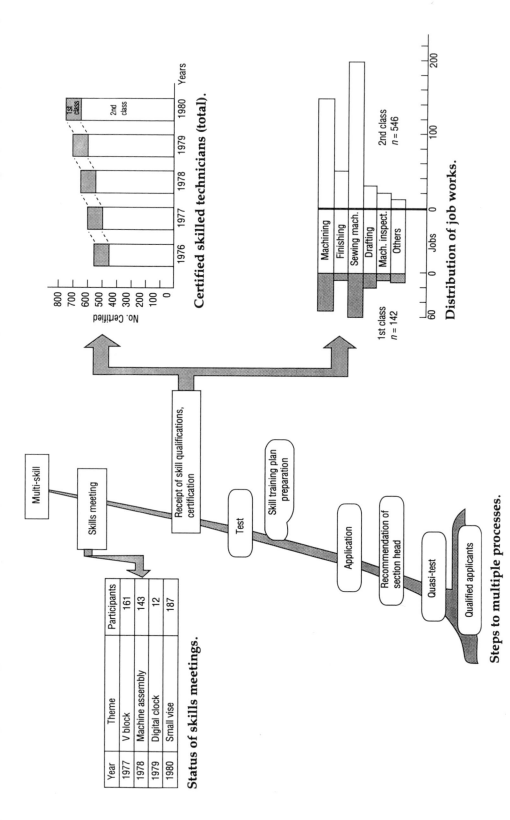

Status of skills meetings.

Year	Theme	Participants
1977	V block	161
1978	Machine assembly	143
1979	Digital clock	12
1980	Small vise	187

Certified skilled technicians (total).

Distribution of job works.

Steps to multiple processes.

FIGURE 16.11. Education of skilled technicians.

193

17

Policy Control

—Control policy to unify corporate activities.

THE NECESSITY FOR POLICY CONTROL

It is necessary for the survival and growth of a company that corporate activities be unified on the basis of a policy that is determined by top management. TQC activities are those that encourage total participation. It is necessary that all the people in the company understand the purpose for which they are performing their activities. Problems occur when:

- The company president's policy (business policy) is not communicated from top to bottom, resulting in insufficient interdepartmental unity.

- Top management's policy is not specific enough, so people do not know what to do.

- Department managers are slow to develop their policies and change them often.

- Insufficient thought and analysis are devoted to previous years' problems, and policy is based mainly on wishes for the future.

Professor Ikezawa of Waseda University mentions the following problems that can occur during TQC introduction.

- Company policy is unclear and is not transmitted to all departments.
- Even if a policy exists, there is no checking to see whether it has been achieved.
- There is no policy control that checks problems of the past to see which ones need to be dealt with by the new policies.

It is necessary, then, for company management to continue improving the level of work in the coming business period by deploying a unified business policy using PDCA cycles to assure achievement of targets and standardization of work. This is the meaning of policy control.

Policy control is thus a systematic activity that is based on creating harmony among various jobs in regard to policy, involving planning (Plan); dissemination, with steps to ensure compatibility with the annual management policy (president's policy) (Do); and checking the results (Check) for necessary action (Act) to achieve the policy. This means establishing a company theme and management ideas for short-, mid-, and long-term plans. The Deming Prize Audit checklist lists policy at the top. Policy is checked for the following points:

- Policy for management, quality, and QC
- How policies are determined
- The reasonableness and consistency of policies
- The use of statistical methods
- How policies are communicated and disseminated
- The level of achievement of these policies
- The relationship to long-term and short-term plans

Policy control must be based on the following items in order to be implemented effectively.

1. *Clarify* top management policy to assure the thorough dissemination of policy deployment based on a clearly identified policy throughout all departments and all levels, so that everyone understands it well.
2. *Plan*—Create a specific plan for each individual's share of the load.
3. *Check results*—Check the status of achievement.
4. *Control*—Isolate problems in order to base the next business term's plan on them.

THE PURPOSE AND EFFECTS
OF POLICY CONTROL

Policy control is really a breakthrough control activity that will analyze problems to achieve upper management policies, as well as each department's policy, and that devises new methods of achievement in order to deal with shortcomings. Policy control can fill the gap between what should be and

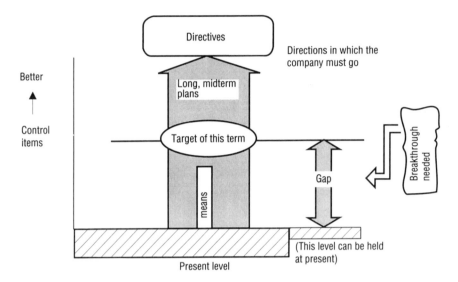

FIGURE 17.1. Purpose of policy control.

what can be done, using PDCA cycles and deployment of actions based on a relationship between the targets and the means to achieve them. This can be done throughout all departments and levels of the company (see Figure 17.1). We can say that the purpose of policy control is as follows.

The Purpose of Policy Control

1. Major points are clarified as business targets and the means to achieve them are assured for effective action taking.
2. QC-like problem solutions are used for the major points.
3. The president's policies are deployed to department heads to achieve better understanding, smoother communication, and a more organic top-to-bottom tie-in.

The following effects can be attained using policy control.

10 Effects of Policy Control

1. Management targets can be achieved more surely and more effectively.
2. The company's structure can be enhanced by improving the QA system and new-product development system.
3. An improved level of control and quality of work can be achieved.
4. The work that needs to be done is clearer, which improves an individ-

ual's understanding of his or her position and role in the total organization.

5. A clearer understanding of workload sharing in vertical and horizontal interrelationships will thoroughly penetrate the ideas of top management.

6. Problem solving will be carried out with an emphasis on the most critical problems.

7. A more systematic job is possible because it will be based on facts and data.

8. Higher worker morale and motivation will improve human-resources development.

9. More timely adaptation to changes in the business environment will speed modifications of targets, plans, and work methods.

10. An overall improvement in companywide TQC activities.

HOW TO IMPLEMENT POLICY CONTROL

The PDCA cycle is emphasized in policy control. PLANS are made on the basis of a policy, and are then put into effect (DO) and CHECKED for results to analyze the causes of the problems, if any, for the purpose of improvement (ACT). The policy control procedure is thus to set the president's policy and the way the specific policy will be deployed to department heads (see Figure 17.2).

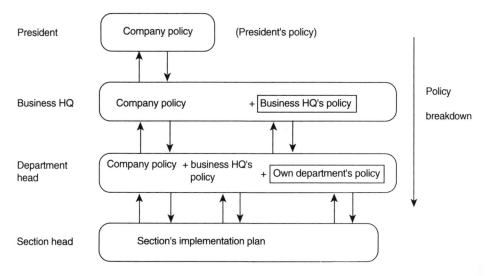

FIGURE 17.2.   Implementing policy control.

TABLE 17.1. Policy planning terminology.

	POLICY		
Term	*Emphasis*	*Target*	*Means (weighted)*
Meaning	Shows direction and placement of weight for management activity to achieve this term's target	Numerical expression of targets (or goals); if not numerical, then in specifics	Means for achievement of target concept, strategy for solution

Procedure for Setting President's Policy

Step 1. *Clarify the tasks of this business period on the basis of the president's midterm management plan.*

1. Pick out tasks for this business period.
2. Decide which tasks are the most critical.

Step 2. *Clarify in-house tasks.*

1. Analyze any differences between the previous policy targets of the president and actual performance, and the planned numbers of the previous business period, for quality (Q), profit and cost (C), production and sales (D), safety (S), and education and personnel (M).
2. Analyze trends and features of the performances of the past few years.
3. Look for tasks that can be completed in this business period (management tasks, structural improvement tasks).
4. Decide which tasks are the most critical.

Step 3. *When changes in external conditions are newly foreseen, define new tasks.*

1. Discern changes in politics, the economy, society, international relations, competition, and the market.
2. Single out newly foreseen tasks.
3. Decide which tasks are most critical.

Step 4. *Clarify companywide tasks on the basis of thorough discussions between the president and department heads.*

1. Select from those tasks that are most critical the ones that are emergencies, are in need of improvement, or are long-term.
2. Decide which tasks are the most critical.

Step 5. *Make a final decision on the critical tasks and divide them up between the corporate headquarters and the main offices of a business group.*

After the completion of each of Steps 1 through 4 above, the tasks that are considered most critical are communicated to the company headquarters or the business group offices.

Step 6. *Plan the president's policy based on the critical tasks.*

Step 7. *Issue a policy paper.*

1. Issue a policy paper emphasizing control items and targets (see Table 17.1).
2. Itemize as much as possible to aid comprehension.

How Department Heads Can Enact Policy Control

A. *Planning a policy (PLAN)*

* Policy planning for department heads

Step 1. *A self-analysis of previous performance to understand the problems.*

1. Items in the previous targets that were not achieved.
2. Process problems.
3. The causes for the lack of full achievement and an analysis of them.

Step 2. *Selecting a policy theme for your own department for the year.*

1. Take into consideration the annual business plan, upper-management policy, and your own performance.
2. Collect data on the economy, on competition, and on profitability, etc.
3. Study the relationships between management indices and the selected themes.
4. Identify basic work indicators and relevant themes.
5. Look for compatibility with upper-management policies.
6. Analyze the role of your own department and clarify your own themes and roles.
7. Select themes based on your own capabilities, both with respect to departmental matters and with respect to people (trying to keep within 10 items by emphasizing the most important of them).

Step 3. *Determine your own departmental policies based on the themes selected and on upper-management policies.*

1. Put upper management's policies up front and quantify their expectations.
2. Determine your own policies in terms of ability to manage.
3. Have your section heads offer opinions and solutions that can be added to the policy.

    4. Set targets that are within reach.

    5. Look at your own policy to discover contradictions with upper-management policy or with the president's policy.

Step 4. *Set control items and evaluate the results.*

    1. Set control items so that the results can be evaluated.

    2. Determine the criteria for target values and checking methods, and for taking action on these control items.

    3. Set targets that are within reach. Unachievable levels are meaningless.

Step 5. *Check your own policy with upper management, section heads, and related departments.*

    1. This improves understanding of upper management's and other departments' policies.

    2. Check the achievability of targets with section heads and with related departments.

    3. Match the targets and the means to achieve them, and check relationships with upper management, section heads, and related departments.

    4. Check to see that your own policies are more concretely developed than those of upper management and that the policies of section managers below you are more concretely spelled out than yours.

    5. If necessary, prepare (in writing) explanations of the reasons for present problems and an analysis of the true causes.

    6. Prepare an implementation plan for the department heads.

      a. Prepare a plan for your own actions.

      b. Prepare a plan for enacting the policies of section heads; pay attention to the who, what, when, where, why, and how.

      c. Establish a method to check the results of the work of your subordinates.

B. Preparing an action plan (section heads)

Step 1. *Review the current status of policies of your department head in order to better understand problems.*

    1. Check the quality, cost, delivery, safety, and morale (Q, C, D, S, and M).

    2. Check control methods.

    3. Handle requests from other departments.

Step 2. *Check the effect of your own problem-solving activities on others.*

    1. Check to see if the improvement of quality might adversely affect cost, delivery, or safety.

2. Check that improvement of your own section does not adversely affect other departments or sections.
3. Judge and evaluate problems.
   a. Stratify and look at the relationships of problems.
   b. Apply a weighting system to each problem.
   c. Check to see if the problem is one of maintenance control or required improvement.

Step 3. *Confirm your predictions for the future.*
1. Understand the needs and the ideas of your superiors, that is, the heads of the departments.
2. Check your own position with regard to total company plans and departmental plans.
3. Analyze data from the outside, such as engineering data, environmental conditions, and market conditions.

Step 4. *Determine items for action.*
1. Determine items for action based on a detailed understanding of the policies of your department head.
2. Determine items for action to solve problems that will achieve the policies of upper management, and select the best means from the various ones available after comparing and evaluating them.
3. Determine items for action that will solve critical problems in your own section.
4. Determine the degree of achievability of these action items.

Step 5. *Deploy each item in detail in order to determine priorities.*
1. Make a detailed deployment of items for implementation.
2. Check the degree of importance of these items and prioritize them.

Step 6. *Set control items.*
1. Determine control items in order to evaluate the results.

Step 7. *Set targets and determine a schedule for action.*
1. Set targets so that some effort will be required to achieve them.
2. Determine an order of action, and set deadlines.
3. Determine how actions will be shared and who will be in charge.
4. Prepare graphs, checklists, arrow diagrams, bar charts, etc. to follow the level of achievement.

Step 8. *Determine support systems.*
1. Check the need for support systems.

C. *Implementing the policy (DO)*

Step 1. *Clarify the plan of action: department head → section head, section head → group head.*
1. Determine to whom the plan should be explained.
2. The necessity of the plan and the reasons for action should be in writing.
3. Use QC stories to explain, referring to problems, causes, means, and plans of action.

Step 2. *Gain the support of section heads and assistant supervisors.*
1. Offer guidance and education to assure achievement.
2. Clarify which items are to be reported by those in charge.

Step 3. *The people in charge act according to their action plans.*
1. Be responsible for your own work.
2. Always know the status of the action plan.
3. Report the level of achievement at least once a month to receive further instructions.
4. In case there are variations in results of the plan, make corrections to the plan.

Step 4. *Record the status of the PDCA.*
• Make a record of the essence of the action process and the results.

D. *Confirm and check the results of the action (CHECK)*

Step 1. *Make monthly checks of the differences between targets and actual performance for each policy and for each action item.*
1. Check weekly or monthly, as needed.
2. Check the achievement and level of progress for each policy.
3. Plot in line-graph form in order to check the achievements for each of the control items numerically.
4. Use checklists, bar charts, arrow diagrams, etc.

Step 2. *When there are differences between the policy targets and actual performance, check them against the three cases in Table 17.2.*

Step 3. *Determine the causes for these differences between targets and actual performance and take corrective actions.*
1. The process resulted in a difference—in the way of work, the material, the people, the conditions—so all must be checked (see Figure 17.3).
2. Look at the process for these causes and pick out those that are most critical and need correction (degree of effect).

TABLE 17.2. Cause for non-achievement.

Item	Action plan	Achievement (result)	Causes
Case I	O	X	Action plan was good but action was insufficient.
Case II	X	O	Acted according to plan but plan was poor.
Case III	X	X	Plan and action were poor.

Note: O = good; X = poor

E. Handling (ACT)

Step 1. Take corrective actions to smoothly make up for gaps in achievement. A monthly check will reveal where achievement is insufficient and where a plan for recovery needs to be acted upon.

Step 2. Analyze the differences between targets and actual results to prevent these from occurring again. Find what caused the difference and take corrective action so that this does not happen again. In other words, improve the work habits that caused this difference.

Step 3. Improve the way one works. In policy control, we self-reflect each month on our plan and look for ways to improve our work.

CONTROL ITEMS

Policy control is an activity done to achieve targets in a variety of business functions (cost, production, delivery, safety, personnel, etc.), but centers

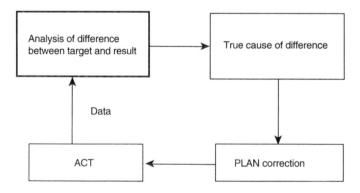

FIGURE 17.3. Checking results and correcting.

mainly around the quality function. It emphasizes the direction of the business by the setting of targets and the planning, acting, and checking during every business period (short-, mid-, or long-term, or any other business period), as we have said before. Thus, control items are necessary to evaluate the level of achievement of the target, and they are necessary for policy control.

JIS Z 8101, *QC Terminology*, calls a control point:

- An item that is the subject of control in order to maintain product quality. For example, electrical current density, voltage, solution temperature, solution composition, etc. in the case of electrolysis, or how cutting tools are mounted, cutting speed, tooling set-up, etc. for machine-tool work.

- An item that is the subject of control, giving rational control over TQC activities. For example, a control item will exist for each job. Such a control item could be called a yardstick for the actions necessary to judge the progress of a job or the achievement of a work function of a department, which is normally expressed as its characteristic value.

It is important in policy control to increase the level of each process to create better results. Thus, for each point that is analyzed for differences between targets and results and to find the causes and a way to improve the process (nature of work, method of work), control items become necessary for improvement. Thus, they are a yardstick, a necessary measure to evaluate results. If the set of control items is inadequate, it is difficult to achieve proper improvement, and quality or profit may not be achieved. Control items that are used in policy control for TQC are quite complex. Table 17.3 gives some examples of these control points.

IMPORTANT CONSIDERATIONS IN POLICY CONTROL

Please note the following three considerations.

Considerations for Policy Control

1. Set tasks that will improve the corporate structure and keep on improving them.
2. Determine control items and targets for each policy and business period under control.
3. At the end of the business period, think carefully about the results during that period.

When creating a rational planning policy, take into account the following 30 points of concern and/or avoidance.

TABLE 17.3. Examples of control items.

Area / Aim	Whole of business department	Product planning	Product - design engineering	Production	Cost - subcontract control	Sales	Service
Overall (T)	• Operational profit • Profitability • Market share • Break-even point • TQC level • No. of new products	• No. of completion of new product plans • No. of proposals • No. of new business/products • No. of ideas	• No. of completions of new product plans • No. of completions of new product design • No. of completions of new product prototype • No. of completions of new product sales start • No. of completions of package design	• Rejection rate • Rate of assurance of process capability	• Profitability per product • Pay line • Defect - rate at shipment	• Market share per prod. • Market per prod. group • Achievement of sales target • Order intake outside of target • Rate of export	• No. of service depot
Quality (Q)	• Rate of occurrence of critical problem • No. of complaints	• Complaints due to planning • No. of advanced tech. developments • No. of advanced tech. • No. of completion analyses	• No. of complaints due to design • No. of complaints due to new products • No. of complaints due to patents • No. of complaints due to patent application • No. of complaints due to metal mold trial • No. of complaints due to standards, specs. set • No. of complaints due to tech. registration • Rate of design change	• No. of complaints due to product • Rejection of shipped products • Process rejection rate • No. of process development • No. of equipment development • No. of no-inspection • No. of hours of down time	• No. of complaints due to subcontracts • No. of complaints due to suppliers • Rate of product rejections • Rate of rejected supply parts • Rate of shipment rejections • Rate of no-inspection	• No. of complaints due to sales	• No. of complaints, use/installation • No. of claims handled • No. of repairs • No. of seminars • No. of seminar attendants • No. of service depots established
Cost (C)	• Amount/rationalization • Cost rate • Variance (rate) • Value added per worker • Fixed expenses • Conformance to budget	• No. of studies of cost/needs • Development efficiency	• Amount/design rationalization • Amount/package design rationalization • Amount/R&D • Achievement of target design cost • No. of design changes • Rate of parts commonality	• Amount/production rationalization • Rate of automation • Operation rate • Reject loss amount • Value added produced • Production cost rate • Production per worker • Rate of productivity • Loss cost ratio • Assembly rejections	• Amount/purchase rationalization • Amount/VE • Rate of variance • Fixed expense • Amount/rationalization	• Sales cost • Discount rate • Rate of outside sales • Rate of sales visits • Product turnover • Fixed cost per salesman	• Amount/claim loss • Rate/claim cost • Cost of repairs • Cost of replacement • Cost of returns • Cost of refunds • Cost of returned rejects
Delivery/ Quantity (D)	• Production volume • Sales volume • Inventory • New product sales • Achievement of planned production • Productivity increase	• No. of user research • No. of market research • No. of completion study • New product sales • Development time • Rate of contribution of new product sales	• No. of sales of new product • Time required for design • Time required for prototype • Time required for pre-production • Time required for package design • No. of drawings issued • Time required for metal mold	• In-house production • Production per hour • Excess inventory • Rate of in-house prod. • No. of completion of prototype • New products production ratio • Plant utilization • Achievement of planned production	• Amount of outside production • Delay of supplies • Outside inventory • In-process inventory • Delivery for inspection • Rate of supplier delivery • No. of supplier rejections • Achievement of delivery • Plant utilization	• Rate of promised delivery • New product sales • Export amount • New market share • Rate of achievement/target accounts • Rate of new account visit • Rate of new inquiry • Rate of follow-up of inquiry • Achievement of planned sales	• Repair cost • After-market sales • After-market inventory • No. of sales route development • No. of sales depot development • No. of new OEM's
Safety (S)	• Degree • Intensity	• No. of accidents • No. of pollution complaints • Achievement of pollution regulation					
Morale (M)	• No. of proposals • No. of completion of theme • Rate of proposals	• No. of qualifications obtained • Score of QC circle evaluations • No. of proposals per worker	• No. of tech. note issues • No. of theme completions/QC team • No. of uses of personal CPU	• No. of standards issued • No. of revisions of standards • Amount/improvement effect			

30 Points of Consideration for Policy Control

A. *General*

1. Top management takes leadership of policy control.
2. Have all employees recognize what each one needs to do.
3. Clarify the responsibility and authority of each person.
4. PDCA cycles must be performed many times. Once is not enough.
5. Policy control should result in a change in the way one works.
6. Policy control cannot succeed unless there is daily control.
7. The morale and spirit of all employees is needed to achieve the targets.
8. A top management diagnosis needs to be made in order to follow up on the indicated items.
9. Do not attempt policy control unless you can support the system of checking.
10. Improve the way in which policy control is carried out.

B. *Planning policy*

11. Targets cannot be achieved by mere activity. Specific means must be chosen.
12. Emphasize that which is most important.
13. There must be "do's" for every action planned.
14. Use strategies and tactics in planning.
15. Put creativity and ideas into the plan.
16. Plans should not stop at an idea. The purpose of a plan is that X achieves Y by doing Z.
17. When planning, in-depth dialogue must be engaged in constantly.
18. Play catch-ball, that is, passing back and forth, from top to bottom and from side to side between related departments and sections.
19. As policy is disseminated downward, it must become more and more specific.
20. Let those who are in charge at the lower levels devise the specific means for achieving the policies and targets given to them.
21. Be clear about control items, target values, and deadlines.
22. Produce a good set of control items to evaluate the level of achievement of the policies.
23. Evaluation of the achievements must be numerical, otherwise the control items do not really exist.

C. *Implementing policy*

24. Actions must take place more and more at the lower levels.

25. Do not give up on something as being unachievable until action has been taken.

D. *Checking and actions on policy*

26. Before planning, begin by checking, that is, reflecting on and analyzing, problems of the past year.

27. When checking policies, give more weight to the process than to the results.

28. In order to take action, evaluate a process as being either good or poor.

29. Do not forget about the monthly follow-ups, repeating the PDCA cycle at least once a month.

30. All members should do their best at their positions so that their actions contribute to solving the problems.

POLICY CONTROL AT RICOH

The experience of Ricoh (as told by T. Hirakawa, assistant department head, Control Department, Ricoh) is a good example of policy control.[21] Hirakawa's account occupies the remainder of this chapter.

*   *   *

Foreword

Policy control is one of the most important devices for managing a company and is one of the most critical tasks for top management.

Policy control can affect a company's performance, particularly in these days of severe and complex business environments. It can either make or break a company in some cases, particularly in the mid to long term. Policy control can take a large and risky project forward to success because its dominant theme is the survival of the company.

To respond to today's low-growth economy, a way must be devised to continue in business in low-growth as well as in high-growth conditions. Of course, at our company, the way in which policy control is operated has undergone change. When TQC was first introduced (prior to 1971), policy and its control were really inadequate for quality and for proper deployment.

The policy was planned by some staff members and was relatively one-sided because it lacked specifics and was not tied in with any particular actions. Further, results were neither checked nor reflected upon when the next plan was undertaken.

Some time passed after introducing TQC before real improvement was begun. Then improvements in our company's policy control were made, and in 1975 we received the Deming Prize. Our policy control has been established well enough to withstand the test of time. The points that we improved were:

- Our method of policy planning
- Our method of control
- Preparing of an underlying framework for policy control
- Our review of policy systems

How to Do Policy Control

A. An outline

Policy can be divided into basic policy and period policy at our company.

- *Basic policy*—Management policy that indicates the basic attitudes of the company towards business and its environment.
- *Period policy*—Indicates a policy and plan for a certain time period that includes a long-term view, and this is communicated as action items through the section heads.

A basic policy includes management policy and management's basic regulations, which determine the action criteria and establish a basic policy for each function and the method for each supervisor in charge. Figure 17.4 shows our method of policy control.

B. Creating a mid-term plan

Based on a long-term plan, there are companywide mid-term plans and mid-terms plans for particular business areas.

1. *Long-term vision*—Ten-year plan reviewed annually
2. *Mid-term plan*—Three-year plan reviewed annually
3. *Business plan*—For each department based on the management plan
4. Procedure for creating a mid-term plan

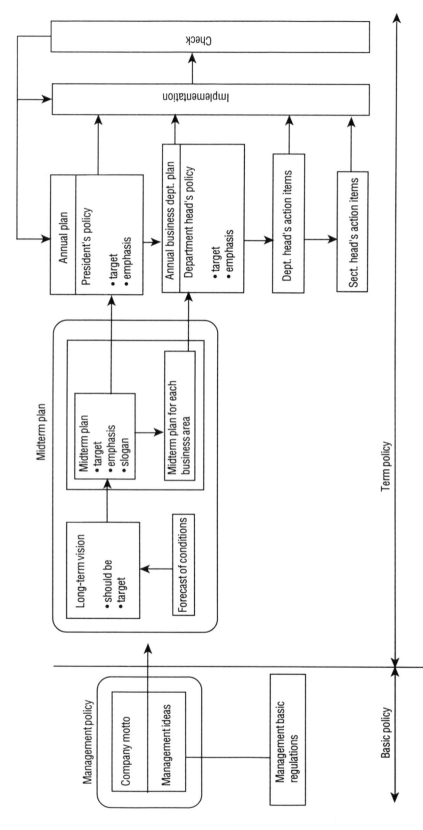

FIGURE 17.4. Outline of policy control.

The president's top management decides on the mid-term plan based on the long-term vision. Then, each department makes its own mid-term plan. These plans undergo diagnosis and guidance from top management at the audit meeting prior to receiving approval. Long-term visions and mid-term plans are presented by the president at a strategy meeting. This meeting is attended by managers and includes the section heads of one's own company and perhaps related companies. Booklets describing the plan in greater detail are distributed.

C. Annual deployment of policy

Figures 17.5 and 17.6 are an outline of the annual policy deployment and action plan.

1. In planning the president's policy and the business group head's policy, an annual plan is based on previous problems, new problems, and other changes in conditions. It is presented during the annual management strategy meeting. The business policy is then based on this. The policy of the head of the business group will include a target, certain emphases, and an improvement plan and will be determined by management at the top management audit meeting. They will look for adequacy of the targets or of the specific method. A theme is assigned to each top manager. There are control items for the business department head to check for achieving the items that are considered most critical.

   Control items will emphasize the method of control, including quality, cost, and delivery (Q, C, and D), and resources that will supply clear data are used to help judge one's own work and action-taking. Other items that are included in the control items are those requests that will delegate authority to department heads for Q, C, and D.

2. Department heads' policy is based on the business department policy. It is planned with discussions among section heads and is determined through an evaluation by the head of the particular business department. This evaluation checks with upper-level policies and draws on relations with other departments to make sure that the theme problems are approached in common ways and by consensus.

3. Section heads' policy is based on the department head policy and is planned through a discussion with other group heads. Approval is through the department head.

4. Policy presentation meetings are used to better disseminate these specific plans and procedures for action. The business department head's policy presentation and the department head's policy presentation are usually held every year.

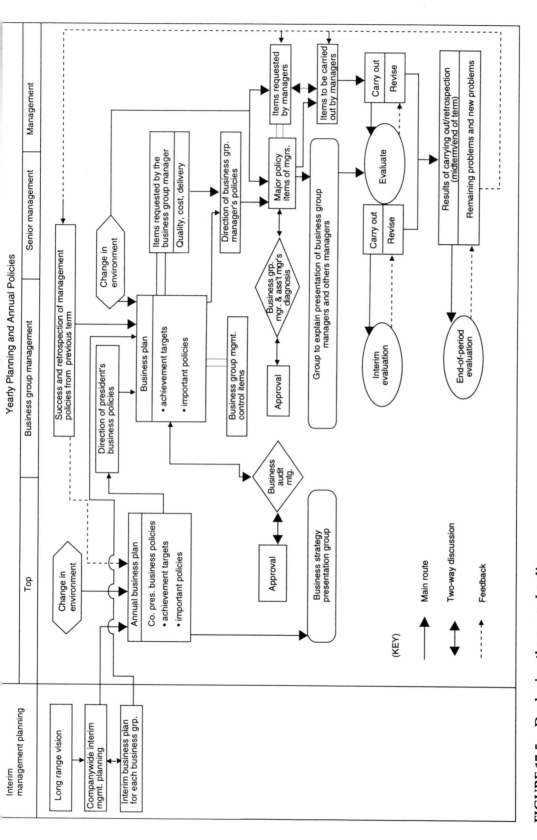

Yearly Planning and Annual Policies

FIGURE 17.5. Deploying the annual policy.

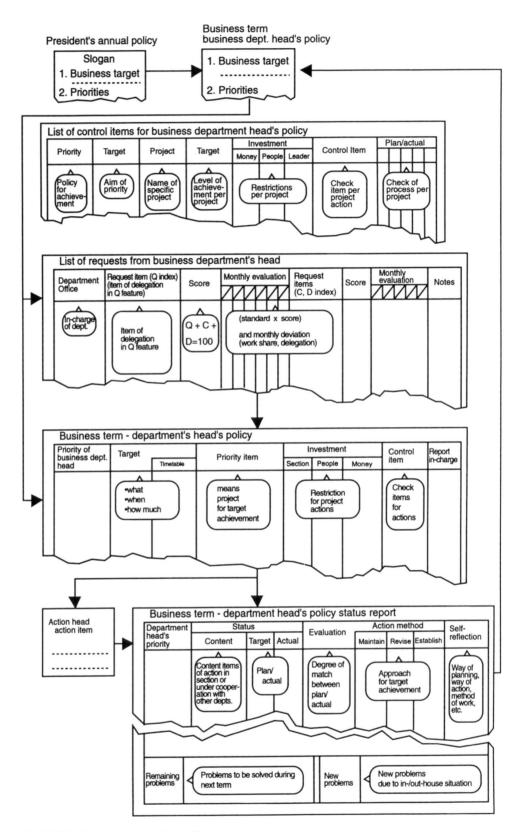

FIGURE 17.6. Action plan chart.

TABLE 17.4.   Evaluation meetings.

Name	Subject	Attending meeting	Frequency
(1) Management audit	Each business department or branch office	President, top manager	2 per yr
(2) Business department head's evaluation	Each department	Business depart-ment head	2 per yr
(3) Department head's evaluation	Each section	Department head	2 per yr

D.   Evaluating policy achievement

It is necessary to check achievements against targets and to tie the results of this to actions. Managerial improvements can be determined by dialogue both vertically and horizontally throughout the company.

- Subjects to be evaluated:
  1. Performance versus target
  2. Work methods or process of achievement
- Purpose of evaluation:
  1. Achieving policy and targets
  2. Timely correction of plans and actions to instigate changes
  3. Improvement and guidance directions
- Method:
  1. Prepare performance report
  2. Use evaluation reports from upper management

Table 17.4 summarizes the types of evaluation meetings.

Six Elements for Supporting Policy Control

The method of policy control described above has enabled our company's policy control to attain a certain level of effectiveness, but it cannot function entirely by itself. Some major elements that support our company's policy control are as follows.

1. The quality of our policies is supported by ideas that are based on facts, and that include the viewpoints of others and promote the Golden Rule. Policy must be based on facts and be specific.

Many policies are achieved only by participation of the workers. The policies that we desire to achieve must be understood by everyone, and this is done through dialogue. The results must be good for the participants.

2. It is necessary to have a business plan system and audit diagnosis meetings that support policy control. Our policy control system is combined with a business planning system. In the past, the policy was independent of business control, and it tended to be abstract and rather formal.

The business plan system and the policy control system were integrated for improvement. As a result they have been more closely related to our daily work and have thus become more effective. Further, applying the audit diagnosis to policy control improves communication between job levels, is a better check for progress, and helps promote action and better control cycles, giving better results.

3. Delegation of authority and an exclusive staff for policy control support the effort. Our company's organization is based on sharing authority. We have nearly 20 business departments and our people in the headquarters as well as the various business department heads perform their work based on the authority that is delegated to them. A few staff members are placed in each business department to look after the promotion of policy control. Thus, sharing authority and a dedicated staff related to practical policy planning, daily control, and promoting problem solution help achieve our targets.

4. A high QC level and systematic education support policy deployment. It is important to improve the level of QC language and ideas within the company. That is one objective of policy control, and as a result policy control was accepted smoothly. Our company's education system runs under the motto, "Education is the most important theme at Ricoh," and it contributes to policy deployment.

5. To promote realization of policies, we have a plan capability development system. This is based on voluntary use and dialogue in order to develop our human resources. Each worker is informed of upper management policy and sets his or her own target as a challenge for achievement. This was originally part of the personnel system but it also contributes to realizing policies.

6. QC circles for participation by everyone provide support for policy control. Currently we have 550 QC circles. These small-group activities are normally voluntary, but themes that relate to the business department's policy are often selected for these groups. This helps to activate participation by everyone for policy control.

As explained above, the system and its administration cannot be effective alone. It is necessary to have supportive measures as well.

Some Cautions for Policy Control

The list below contains some cautionary points that our company considers in using policy control.

- Policies are specific in terms of direction and action criteria.
- There is emphasis on reflecting upon the current period in order to take care of unresolved problems and new problems in the coming business period.
- Policy is carried through from the upper levels down to the lower levels, but it is not only this top-to-bottom relationship that is important. The horizontal relationship is also important. This improves the awareness of accountability for policy control.
- Policy needs to emphasize the who, what, when, where, why, and how, and must be as specific as possible to avoid being considered empty words.
- Evaluation methods need to be set that will promote the challenging of even higher targets.
- To improve comprehension of the policy, it is explained using data in terms that are understandable at every job level.

In Conclusion

The effects of policy control are both tangible and intangible. We can summarize them as follows.

- Improved level of organized activities.
- Using control cycles, we set conditions to challenge higher and higher targets.
- A common awareness of problems and motivation is achieved through dialogue and diagnosis.
- Policy deployment is tied with human resource development.
- Policy control improves corporate structure because of specific project control.

Our policy control system is not yet complete and continues to be revised and followed up on the basis of comparisons of our performance with our plans. We think that an action that is planned ahead is better than 100 actions made afterward. We feel very strongly about seeking continuous improvement so that better policy control will assure our company's future and the smooth operation of our management.

*   *   *

18

Cross-Functional Management

—Communicate horizontally throughout the organization to prevent people from thinking only of their own groups.

WHAT IS CONTROL BY DIVISION?

Making a profit is the number-one job of managers. Without profit, employees cannot be paid and nothing can be returned to society. When making a profit, a vision and a business plan must be prepared that include a strategy and policy based on a long-term profit plan. This is first. Second is that management must be done in such a way as to achieve this efficiently. The TQC subsystems of long- and mid-term business planning and policy deployment are the answers to the first item, and control by division and control by function are answers to the second item.

When organizing the management of a company it is necessary to have departments, such as general administration, finance, personnel, R&D, design, production engineering, production, inspection, and sales and marketing, which are operated with the concept of control by division. Control by division means performing work according to a setup that will achieve the function and role of the department, evaluating the results against that target, and taking action when needed—in other words, going through the cycle of PDCA for control and for raising the level of work improvement.

The How-To's of Division Control

The departments have their own particular roles and functions. These are written down in the job descriptions of the departments and sections, but often they are not detailed enough. Function deployment is therefore recommended to clarify the role and function of each department.

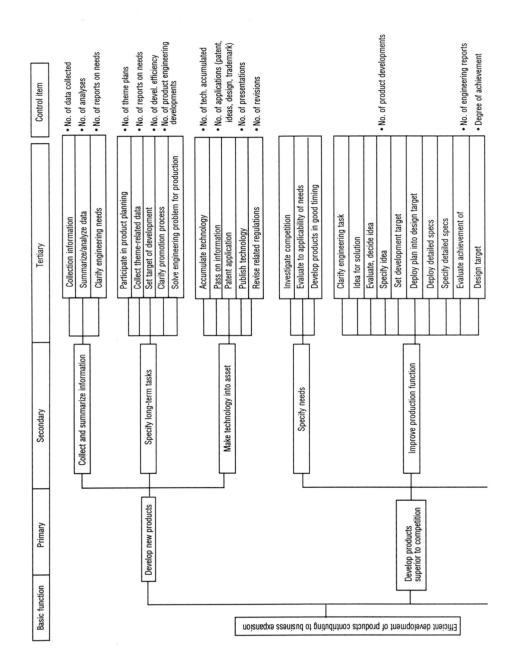

Basic function	Primary	Secondary	Tertiary	Control item
		Collect and summarize information	Collection information Summarize/analyze data Clarify engineering needs	• No. of data collected • No. of analyses • No. of reports on needs
	Develop new products	Specify long-term tasks	Participate in product planning Collect theme-related data Set target of development Clarify promotion process Solve engineering problem for production	• No. of theme plans • No. of reports on needs • No. of devel. efficiency • No. of product engineering developments
		Make technology into asset	Accumulate technology Pass on information Patent application Publish technology Revise related regulations	• No. of tech. accumulated • No. of applications (patent, ideas, design, trademark) • No. of presentations • No. of revisions
Efficient development of products contributing to business expansion	Develop products superior to competition	Specify needs	Investigate competition Evaluate to applicability of needs Develop products in good timing	
		Improve production function	Clarify engineering task Idea for solution Evaluate, decide idea Specify idea Set development target Deploy plan into design target Deploy detailed specs Specify detailed specs Evaluate achievement of Design target	• No. of product developments • No. of engineering reports • Degree of achievement

218

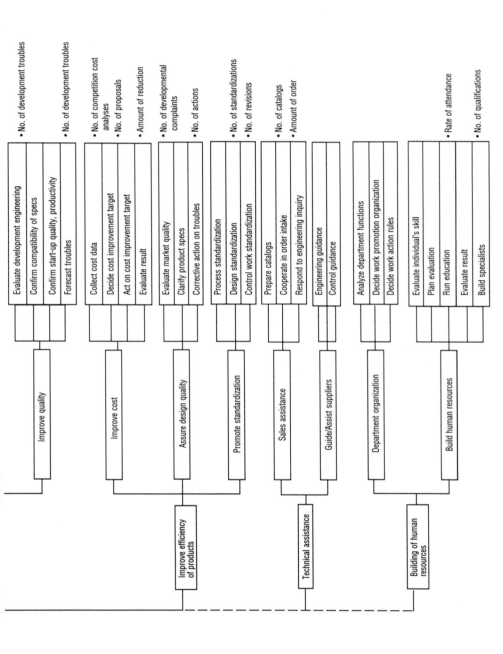

FIGURE 18.1. Example of function deployment.

First, this method clarifies the basic function of the division and continues on to detailed work functions down to second and third tiers in a tree-like diagram. This is called a system chart. Then, the results and the level of achievement for the work are evaluated against the detailed functions as they have been deployed. The basis of QC is checking results and then understanding the good and the bad of the process and taking corrective action. Thus, functions and control items are to be matched, and those that are most critical must be arranged in a list of control items. Figure 18.1 shows such an example of function deployment in the development department of M Electric Company, department S.

In divisional control we have both daily control and policy control. See Figure 18.2.

Daily control encompasses those activities that achieve the work target efficiently in regard to the department's job. This is the most basic activity for divisional control. On the other hand, policy control is an activity to achieve management policies (the president's policy) based on its priorities, as was described in Chapter 17.

WHAT IS CROSS-FUNCTIONAL MANAGEMENT?

"Cross-functional management" is a phrase used in contrast to management by division. In a business organization in Japan, for example, there is a very strong top-to-bottom organizational flow. It could be likened to a strong cord running from corporate office to business headquarters to division to sales office, if we are talking about the sales function. However, there tends to be some group sectionalism in areas such as planning, development, production, and sales.

Cross-functional management is intended to run horizontally through the organization, solving critical problems that involve many departments and making structural improvements to the whole company that are often impossible for one division alone. This is the purpose of cross-functional management.

Cross-functional management is a companywide activity that aims for a target by setting companywide targets for each function, such as quality assurance, cost control, and production control, and then running horizontally through the jobs in the separate departments to unify the understanding of the necessary functions and to achieve cooperation.

The way we choose these function items depends on the type, mode, scale, and management policy of the company. But always, quality, cost, and delivery (Q, C, D), that is, quality assurance, cost or profit control, and production control, are there. Further, we have areas such as order intake control for sales, new product development control, subcontractor control,

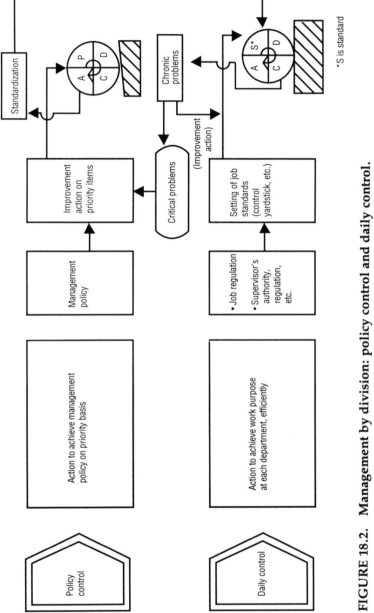

FIGURE 18.2. Management by division: policy control and daily control.

safety control, personnel control, and others. The relationship between cross-functional management and management by division is shown in Figure 18.3.

The following results can be obtained by using cross-functional management.

Results of Using Cross-Functional Management

- Improving the level of quality, cost, delivery, safety, and morale functions (Q, C, D, S, and M) companywide.

- Targeting the achievement of a companywide policy becomes easier and the company structure is enhanced.

- Those actions that connect departments to each other are improved.

- The viewpoint of senior management is broadened to include companywide matters.

- Suggestions come up from the bottom of the organization more frequently.

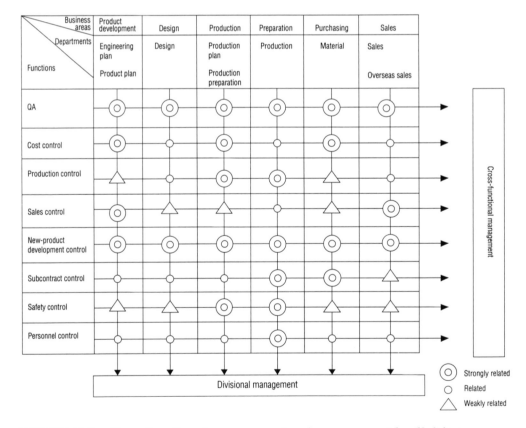

FIGURE 18.3.   **Cross-functional management and management by division.**

HOW TO IMPLEMENT CROSS-FUNCTIONAL MANAGEMENT

Cross-functional management is not a function associated with one department. It has to achieved by the entire company, involving interdepartmental cooperation, a sharing of functions, and a general overall control. Effective cross-functional management can be achieved through the following procedure.

How to Implement Cross-Functional Management

Step 1. Decide on the necessary functions. Study what functions are required for the company to achieve its business targets, then clarify these functions in terms of what is required for improvement and enhancement.

If too many functions are chosen, there may be interference among them. Too few functions can result in a number of departments being involved in only one function, and this can increase complexity. Cross-functional management should be done in a step-by-step manner that begins with two or three main functions, for example, QA and cost control.

Step 2. Form an organization to administer it. Establish "function committees"—for example, a QA function committee—or function conferences to be the organizations that administer cross-functional management. The members of these committees are usually the senior management of the related functions. If need be, department heads can be selected. The committee chairman can be a senior vice-president who might be in charge of the department that is related to the functions being considered. An office is set up for clerical purposes in the department that is most closely related to the functions with problems being addressed. These functions are analyzed together and reported on to the committee.

The committee should have decision-making authority, so it is positioned directly below the top decision-making office, or, in some cases, a management committee.

Step 3. Administration. The committee holds meetings every month, and if necessary may hold separate function meetings. At the monthly meetings solutions to critical problems involving the entire company or a department are discussed, and as a result any items that need to be implemented are given to the appropriate department head. Generally, the following types of items are studied.

- Setting companywide targets, for example, 10 percent reduction in costs throughout the company
- How to achieve targets; interdepartmental coordination
- New product planning, equipment, production, and sales
- Critical subjects that are suggested by the lower levels in the organization
- Eliminating barriers to implementation
- Checking, and taking action on the results
- Checking companywide policy achievement and planning next year's policy
- Other items that are necessary for carrying out functions

The actions for managing by functions are performed by the departments. Thus, the senior management involved must be guided by suggestions from the function committee and report and approve the items that it gets from the committee to make sure that they are handled quickly and accurately. If a problem cannot be solved by one department, a project team is formed. When implementing cross-functional management the following points need to be observed.

10 Points for Effective Cross-Functional Management

1. Delegate authority to the function committee.

2. Each department should have some voice in cross-functional management.

3. Senior management of the functions involved should have a companywide point of view and should act accordingly.

4. The past ways of doing business should be improved upon.

5. The role of each department as to each function should be clarified.

6. Check the function control system to look for areas of improvement.

7. Collect, analyze, and communicate routinely information gathered from both inside the company and outside.

8. Senior management should not push for advantages to their departments only.

9. Looking at too many functions can create interference, so choose only the major functions.

10. Set a target and policy by function to be deployed throughout the entire company.

CROSS-FUNCTIONAL MANAGEMENT AT KOMATSU, LTD.

Our case study of cross-functional management is from Komatsu, Ltd. It was put together by Mr. K. Shimoyamada, the QA department head.[12]

*   *   *

Introduction

Too often, a large company has poor interdepartmental relationships and the efforts being made within the separate departments are inefficiently combined. For this reason our company instituted cross-functional management to improve the handling of interdepartmental problems in an organic way through administration.

The function committee is the center of our activities for promoting cross-functional management efficiency. In this example, we examine our management system for the QA function.

The System of Function Committees

Figure 18.4 illustrates our system. The TQC committee is there for planning, coordinating, and checking all of the QC at Komatsu. The function committee is positioned right below this committee. It is headed by the president, and all its members are from senior management. They are responsible for promoting TQC.

Our company has selected four major functions, the QA function, volume control function, profit control function, and industrial equipment business function.

The QA Concept

1. *The basic concepts of quality assurance.* Our company philosophy is to offer products that match users' needs, and to effectively support the product functions by combining the efforts of the entire Komatsu organization, the related companies, the supplier companies, and the distributors. This is done throughout product planning, development, production, sales, service, and is designed to achieve user satisfaction. This concept is shown in Figure 18.5.

2. *Defining quality assurance.* QA is a systematic activity that lets us offer products to our customers that they can buy without worry and with great satisfaction. Part of the effort is to deploy QA activities based on our company philosophy and to make awareness of QA common to all employees.

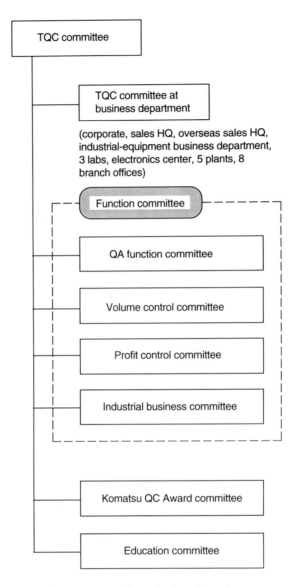

FIGURE 18.4. Role of the function committee.

The QA Function Committee

1. *History*. This committee was formed first as a QA liaison group and developed into the QA function committee in 1980. During the period of the QA liaison group, the QA director was the core of the group and its other members were the heads of related departments. In 1980, the QA director became the chairman and other senior managers be-

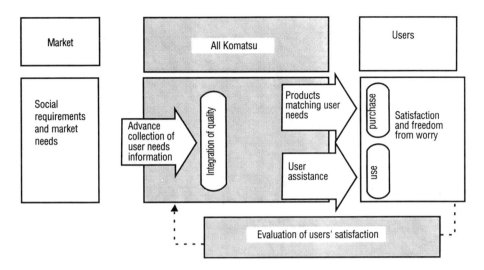

FIGURE 18.5.   The concept of QA.

came members. (See Table 18.1.) They now promote long-term planning as well as discussion and implementation of QA.

2. *Setting up the QA function committee.* This committee was formed with a chairman who was assigned by the president and five members who are senior managers, among whom one or two are from areas with no direct relationship.

  Themes discussed by this committee are first discussed by the function center liaison group, which is right below this committee. The function center liaison group is composed of department heads from development, production, domestic and overseas sales, and the QA department heads of related divisions or subsidiaries.

  For example, the domestic service department is a subcenter which handles and coordinates the sales department for domestic sales. Also, some development- and QA-related tasks are included in the sales area, and so the engineering control department (subcenter representing the engineering area) oversees these types of activities for domestic sales as well as for plants, subsidiaries, and the research laboratory. The corporate production engineering department is a subcenter for the production area which handles and coordinates QA activities in the plant and subsidiaries. Thus, a horizontal type of function is performed by these liaison groups. After themes are discussed they are submitted to the committee and reported to the TQC committee if necessary. A working team is formed according to the difficulty of the task. Its job is to report and to make suggestions to the committee. Figure 18.6 shows such a committee, the function center liaison group, and the team.

TABLE 18.1.   History of QA function committee.

Year	1978	1979	1980	1981	1982	1983
History of committee		QA Liaison Group (Dec. 1978–July 1980)		QA Function Committee		
Members		• QA Director • Related department heads (5–8 people)		• Chairman: QA Director • Members: related directors (5 people)		
Office		QA Department		QA Department		

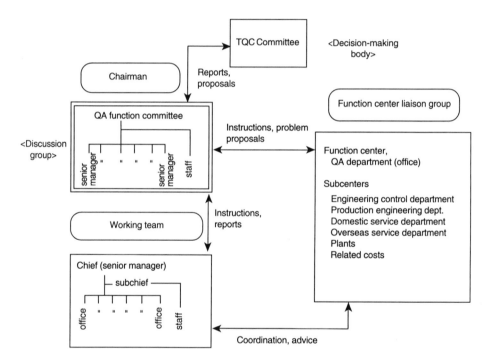

FIGURE 18.6.   Relationships of groups involved in QA.

Administering the QA Function Committee

1. *The role of the QA function committee.* The role of this committee is outlined in our company's regulations for enhancing the position of the committee and the function center liaison group.
   - The purpose of the committee is to improve the way QA is implemented throughout product planning, sales, and service, and to raise the level of QA.

- The committee discusses the following items in order to achieve these purposes and report on them to the TQC committee:
  a. Companywide QA plan
  b. Improving the content of the QA plan
  c. Improving QA and departments in charge

  Improving QA is the point of emphasis and issues such as "how to handle a major complaint" or "individual quality problems" are not handled here.

2. *Administering the function committee's activities.* Figure 18.7 shows how we administer our improvement methods.

   First, we submit the problem. Subcenters submit problems such as what defects in the QA system are causing certain troubles or various control points beginning to show abnormal values. The QA department (office of function committee and function center liaison group) records these problems and proposes them to the function center liaison group. Then, certain items are selected and reported on to the committee.

   For example, problems like whether or not a companywide user satisfaction evaluation system should be established are considered. These problems have by then received a fair amount of up-front work by each subcenter. An improvement plan is submitted to the liaison group to be discussed officially, and then is submitted to the committee to be evaluated, and finally to the senior management level for adjustments. When the plan is approved, the QA department transmits it to the particular line department as a decision item to be actualized.

   Generally, activities by function cannot be performed well unless there is a strong top-to-bottom organization. What we really found after trying out such activities at our company was this need for a strong organization in order to implement work on our themes. As we said before, the company looks at long-term QA plans. This is a problem that many companies have difficulty with. Our example is probably not the best, but we think it is one of the better ones.

   In 1979, our company began studying user satisfaction. Figure 18.8 is an example of function deployment as a result of a survey of user satisfaction with respect to manufacturing, service, and parts (M, S, and P) into the quality features that are used for setting long-term QA targets.

   In this figure the study items for user satisfaction (I) are along the top, and the data on our users' satisfaction (II) and the results of a survey of user satisfaction generally (III) are on the horizontal axis. The results on user satisfaction are marked with a circle (better than the competition), a triangle (the same), or a cross (worse).

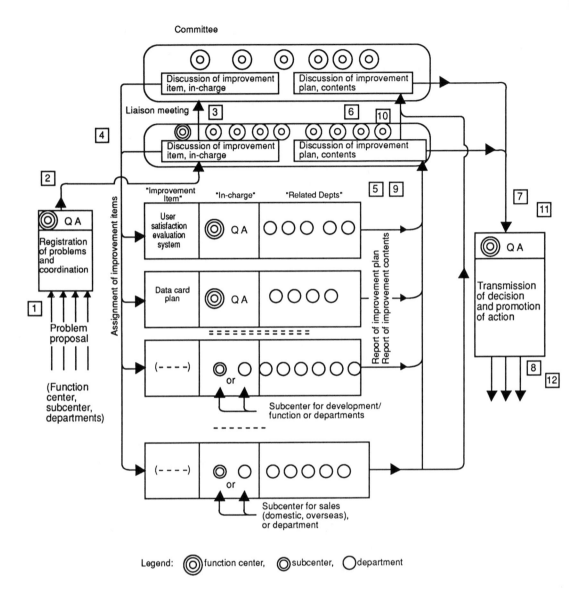

FIGURE 18.7. Administration of improvement process.

When the survey was conducted, we placed weights on each item on the basis of the customer survey. The results tell us that customers strongly desired good work, good reliability, and low cost—which are, after all, rather obvious requirements. In studying user satisfaction for both domestic and foreign markets, our company's product X and a product X made by our competitor called A_1 was marked with a cross for item (3) of manufacturing: less failure and good reliability. A black dot was placed on the intersection of this column with the appropriate

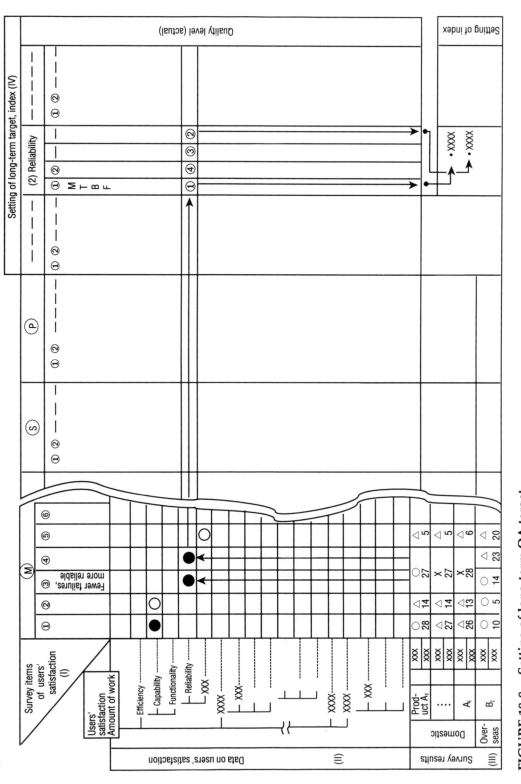

FIGURE 18.8. Setting of long-term QA target.

231

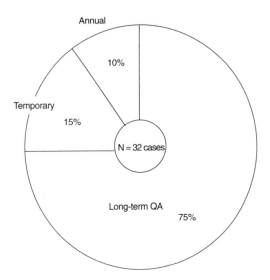

FIGURE 18.9.   Types of theme.

row for user satisfaction. The black dot here is placed next to reliability, indicating that this item needs to be improved in order to strengthen overall satisfaction.

Moving sideways from this black dot, we come to a block of columns for actual level of quality. Reliability had a black dot, and the items for reliability that require some action are found here. If mean time between failures (MTBF) is a problem, then the specific index for its improvement is determined. This is set for reliability and durability for each of the products in regard to its manufacture. Within this we see defects in assembly, number of complaints, mean time between failures, etc. Once these targets are achieved and can be assured, improvement in user satisfaction will occur automatically.

The control items involved here are called QA control points. The direction for future tasks is based on these QA control points, and priority action items are determined in order to solve the problems. Also, the departments in charge are selected, as well as related departments for each theme. The items picked are reviewed annually and are reflected in the next year's activity plan.

3. *Types of themes and controlling activities.* The themes discussed in the function committee are classified into the following three groups, and the ratios among these are shown in Figure 18.9.
   1. Themes for long-term QA planning: 75%
   2. Temporary themes that are chosen by the function committee: 15%

3. Themes that are included every year: 10%

   Example • Rolling over long-term QA plans
   • Annual plans for function committee activities
   • QC diagnosis and QC seminar plans

   It takes three to six months to solve some of these problems, but major ones may take as much as one to two years. There will no doubt be changes in personnel during this period, particularly in the committee office and the action groups, so the reasons for selecting these themes and the targets to be achieved need to be stated clearly in order to have some consistency. An interim check of the actions and timing of reports to the function committee is summarized in the promotion plan chart also, to improve control.

Follow-Up of the Function Committee Activities

A series of activities from the function committee are summarized twice a year and reported to the TQC committee. This is shown in Figure 18.4. Also, an overall summary of these activities receives a QC diagnosis (president's diagnosis) for each function on a companywide level. This is done at the end of each year.

Conclusion

The QA function was used as an example of our company's cross-functional management, but this is still not sufficient in these days of increasing number of types of products, diversification of product specifications, advanced engineering, and product sophistication. A rolling, long-term QA plan is made each year to improve the significance of QA functions. It is done against a background of improving the satisfaction of our users and contributing to society.

*   *   *

19

The QC Audit

—Top management must check itself for progress in promoting TQC activities.

WHAT IS THE QC AUDIT?

One feature of Japanese TQC is the QC audit performed by top management. To cope with changes in business conditions such as increasing sophistication of user demands, diversification, severe competition, a slowing economy, and the need to conserve energy, it is necessary that a good understanding of top management's intentions take hold throughout the company, and the understanding that it is very important to produce high-quality products economically and with good reliability and safety. To this end the dissemination of top management policy and effective TQC must be promoted.

A timely QC audit helps to check the status of QC and to speed up structural improvements in the company. At the same time, it is an effective means to show the enthusiasm of top management, particularly that of the president and the TQC leadership.

Below are the types of QC audits.

Classification by Purpose

1. *For qualification*. It is often necessary to be qualified or certified to sell products that carry, for example, the JIS mark or the ASME manufacturer's approval mark.

2. *For awards*. Awards help achieve a recognition of the level of QC in the company as well as improving the company's image within its industry. These awards include the Deming Prize and the Industrial Technology Award. Companies also give awards to their suppliers—for example, the Toyota QC Award or the Komatsu QC Award.

3. *Checking of processes*. This is done by a buyer to his suppliers. The

buyer checks the control systems and level of engineering of the suppliers and other subcontractors.

4. *For TQC activities*. The degree and status of implementation of TQC is checked.

Classification by Auditor

1. *External*. This can be done by academics or other professionals outside the company. The Deming Prize audit is done by a committee assigned by the Deming Prize committee chairman.

2. *Internal*
   - Done only by people on the inside
   - Done by both internal people and external specialists (QC specialists, director of QC, or people in charge of a subsidiary)

   An in-house QC audit will often use both of the above. Depending on the auditor, there are:
   - president's audits
   - department heads' audits
   - QC staff audits
   - mutual audits by departments

   The QC audit can be defined as an on-site investigation of the level of implementation of QC and of its effects. It points out the good and the bad, and advises of improvement methods and actions that need to be taken. The top management audit is usually a president's or department heads' audit.

THE PURPOSE OF A QC AUDIT

The aim of a QC audit is to check the progress of TQC and to clarify improvement points by objectively evaluating the TQC level to see how much it has enhanced other activities and the structure of the company. We can define the purpose of the audit as follows.

Purpose of a QC Audit
- To confirm by top management the deployment and the practice of company policy and to check for proper action.
- To classify improvement points or targets (what should be) by objectively observing the TQC level.
- To speed up TQC and structural improvements (work attitudes, work methods, and setups).

- To join together the capabilities of all employees to realize targets as effectively as possible.
- To direct communication with employees for better top-to-bottom and bottom-to-top dialogue and morale improvement.

The following results can be expected of a QC audit.

Effects of a QC Audit

- A better understanding of the status of policy deployment or QC in order to improve companywide quality control.
- Dissemination throughout the company of top management's attitude toward QC.
- Direct observations of the status of the company by top management so that better actions can be taken.
- Improvement of top management's understanding of QC.
- Broadening of the view of department and section heads to give them better control.
- Improvement of top-to-bottom communication and improvement of morale.
- Better relationships between top management, staff, and factory workers.

CONDUCTING A QC AUDIT

A QC audit not only directly checks management targets and tasks, but also emphasizes improving work methods and solving problems more efficiently.

It checks to see if in attempting a breakthrough from the present status, the level of control and specific methods are put into practice and are well-controlled. A QC audit is normally conducted in the following steps.

How to Conduct a QC Audit

Step 1. *Clarify the purpose.* A QC audit looks at TQC in general and focuses on the QA system and new product development. When the TQC of a company is new, its focus is on control and improvement. At a company with well-established TQC, the audit looks at the structural enhancements by function or by department. Therefore, the purposes of a QC audit need to be clarified.

Step 2. *Prepare a plan.* The valuable time of the president or other top management must be coordinated. An audit plan is prepared at the start of the year and policies, subject, departments, dates, etc., are determined. This plan is communicated to the related departments as early as possible in order to improve preparation.

Step 3. *Auditors*. Auditors include the president as leader and other top management. If there is a third party involved, i.e., an outside specialist, he or she can help objectively and fairly with the evaluation. When a company is new to QC audits, it tends to have meetings for reporting or troubleshooting. In this case a third-party auditor can be even more effective.

Step 4. *The audit guide*. This shows the purpose, the items, the methods, the dates, the attendees, the schedule, the place, an explanation of the emphasis, and instructions on how to prepare data. Items include:

- Policy deployment
- QA (new product development, new engineering development, etc.)
- Cost control
- Production control
- Improving human resources
- Standardization

Audit by Theme

- Deployment and practice of top management policy.
- Prevention of repeat-complaints and quality problems in critical areas.
- Improvement of the QA system.
- A method of new-product development and control.

Step 5. *Prepare a status explanation sheet*. Actual examples are helpful, particularly when they include charts and logical explanations. Those on the receiving end of the audit need to practice self-reflection and to recognize the results and the problem points. The contents of the explanation sheet can include the following:

- Outline of the department (business group, plant)
- Organization and administration
- The progress of TQC (basic concepts and history)
- Policy deployment
- Human resources (education, training)
- Standardization

- QA (from product planning through to market evaluation)
- Cost control
- Production control
- Overall effects and future planning
- On-site tours, etc.

In addition, order-taking control (sales), safety control, subcontractor control (purchasing), delivery control, and profit control can be added. Those who receive the audit should prepare the following.

- An actual-status explanation sheet
- A detailed explanation of the data
- Daily control data
- Items that are explained on the factory floor (new products, new technology, new simulation, new control systems, improved samples, etc.)

Step 6. *Conduct the audit.* Basic contents of the audit include:
- A greeting from the president
- An explanation of the actual status, followed by Q & A (questions and answers)
- On-site audit and Q & A
- An evaluation by the president and an outside specialist

Table 19.1 shows a sample outline of an audit schedule.

Schedule A (in Table 19.1) shows what the side receiving the audit will prepare and lays out the stages. Schedule B consists of the questions the auditors will ask when they go out to the factory floor. Table 19.2 is a sample list of an audit check sheet, in this case for a Deming Prize audit.

When an auditor asks a question, it is recommended that the answer be explained with facts and material from the daily job.

Step 7. *Notification of results.* The results of the audit are summarized in the audit results opinion report, which is then given to the receiving side. In addition, questions and answers and the contents of the audit are recorded in minutes, which are then distributed to the departments receiving the audit and to other related departments to be used for future reference.

Step 8. *Follow-up of the results.* The side receiving the audit then prepares an improvement plan for the items that have been pointed out by the audit. These are then reported to the TQC promotion department. The progress of this plan is monitored monthly by the TQC committee and at TQC guidance meetings and is followed up at the next TQC audit.

TABLE 19.1. Example of program for presidential audit.

Classification	Items	In-charge	Time (minutes)	Period
	Opening statement	M. C.	5	9:00–9:05
	President's greeting	President	5	9:05–9:10
	1. Outline of branch office 2. TQC progress 3. Policy control	Business department head	20	9:10–9:30
Schedule A	Q & A		15	9:30–9:45
	4. QA	QA Dept. head	25	9:45–10:10
	Q & A		15	10:10–10:25
	Break		15	10:25–10:40
	5. Cost control 6. Production control 7. Human resources 8. Standardization 9. Overall effect and future plan	Section head, department head in charge	20	10:40–11:00
	Q & A		15	11:00–11:15
	On-site explanation		45	11:15–12:00
	Lunch		60	12:00–13:00
	11. On-site tour (per each dept.)	Each dept. head	160 (40 min. × 4 units)	13:00–15:40
Schedule B	Break		15	15:40–15:55
	Overall Q & A		30	15:55–16:25
Instruction/evaluation		President, specialists	30	16:25–16:55
	Business department head's speech	Business dept. hd.	5	16:55–17:00

TABLE 19.2. Deming Prize checklist.

Item	Check points	Item	Check points
1. Policy	1) Management and quality, QC policies 2) Method of policy determination 3) Adequacy of policy, consistency 4) Use of statistical methods 5) Transmission of policy 6) Check of policy and its achievement 7) Long-term plan/short-term relationship	6. Standardization	1) System 2) Method of standardization and revision 3) Actual standardization and revisions 4) Contents of standards 5) Use of statistical method 6) Accumulation of technology 7) Use of standards
2. Organization and administration	1) Clarity of authority delegation 2) Reasonableness of authority delegation 3) Interdepartmental cooperation 4) Committees' activities 5) Use of staff 6) Use of QC circle activities 7) QC audit	7. Control	1) System of cost, volume control 2) Control items, points 3) Use of statistical method, e.g., control chart, etc. 4) Contribution of QC circles 5) Actual control status 6) Control conditions
3. Education, training	1) Plan and practice 2) Awareness for quality, control 3) Statistical methods and its education 4) Effects 5) Education of related companies (especially group companies, subcontractors, suppliers, distributors) 6) QC circle activities 7) Improvement proposal system and reality	8. QA	1) New product development method (quality deployment, reliability design audit, etc.) 2) Safety, P/L prevention 3) Process capability analysis, improvement, process design 4) Inspection 5) Facility, subcontract 6) Purchases, service controls 7) QA system and its audit 8) Use of statistical method 9) Quality evaluation, audit 10) QA status

(continued)

TABLE 19.2. Deming Prize checklist (continued).

Item	Check points	Item	Check points
4. Collection/ dissemination and use of information	1) Collection of outside data 2) Transmission—interdepartmental 3) Speed of data transmission (use of CPU) 4) Arrangement of data (statistical) analysis	9. Effects	1) Measurement 2) Tangible effect quality, service, delivery 3) Costs, profit, safety, environmental, etc. 4) Intangibles, self-prediction and actual
5. Analysis	1) Selection of priority items 2) Adequacy of analysis method 3) Use of statistical method 4) Tie-up with own technology 5) Quality analysis, process analysis 6) Use of analysis result 7) Improvement proposal	10. Future plan	1) Current status and specificity 2) Method to correct defects 3) Future plan 4) Relationship to long-term plan

WHAT TO CONSIDER IN A QC AUDIT

Depending on the way the QC audit is conducted, it can:

- Remain a formality without much substance
- Stop at problem definition without results
- End with cosmetic actions that create a false appearance of achievement

Thus, the QC audit needs to be watched for the following points.

Advice for an Effective QC Audit

- Both the auditor and the receiving side must be in a mood that makes the audit easy to conduct.
- Those receiving the audit must be honest in their attitudes and not hide their faults or present doctored samples.
- Avoid verbal explanations. Report with data, analyses, control charts, standards, etc., as well as a QC story.
- Do not stop at the problem-finding stage, but try to discover good points as well.
- Do not be formal, but get down to the realities of the daily job.
- Do not be biased. Depend on the facts to make correct judgments.
- Do not stop at the results, but look for ways to improve the process (work methods, procedures, setup).
- Evaluate how work experience is accumulated in order to promote self-confidence.
- Do not be abstract when pointing things out, but rather show specific improvement methods.
- Items that are pointed out should be put into an improvement plan and should be followed up.

A PRESIDENTIAL QC AUDIT AT PENTEL CO., LTD.

The presidential audit at Pentel Co., Ltd. is here discussed by Z. Shimada, head of the TQC promotion office.[2m] Pentel develops and manufactures ballpoint pens, mechanical pencils, leads, etc. It has an active TQC program and strong consumer orientation, and recently has been using computers and robots as well.

*   *   *

Introduction

Our company began its presidential QC audit in 1978. Since 1973 all members of our company had studied TQC and its implementation. In 1976 we were awarded the Deming Prize, but by 1978 the mood of the company was a little too easygoing because we had achieved our initial targets.

Also at this time we had many new employees who had not gone through the experience of competing for the Deming Prize. A presidential QC audit was adopted to maintain our practice of QC and to improve the level of our TQC.

Outline of the Presidential QC Audit

The audit is conducted twice a year at 22 operating units in Japan. It usually takes one full day per operating unit regardless of the number of employees there. The audit is based on the Deming Prize audit, Schedules A and B.

1. *Schedule A*. First, the following presentations are made by the unit that is the subject of the audit.
    1. Department head presents a CAPDCA based on the four pillars of quality, delivery, cost, and human resources (including QC circles). This is done under the name of a TQC progress history.
    2. The receiving end presents the major themes of the past six months to one year that have contributed to advancing the policies of the department head. The themes are presented by two or three people who work for the department head (production section head, sales department section head, or similar classification). A QC story is given on how the job improvements were planned and the results of the presenter's own particular job are covered. This QC story is an established presentation format.
2. *Focus of the auditor*. A Schedule A audit is based on the presidential QC audit Schedule A checklist. It includes the following points.
    - Auditors check to see if the presentation is based on facts or not; look at the material that is distributed.
    - The differences between actual performance and targets are not analyzed very well at most departments other than the production department, so this is often a point of focus.
    - When a work method is changed, auditors must confirm that a revision of the work standard has been made.
    - Auditors check any remaining problems and see if future plans include specific actions for these or not.
    - Auditors pick up practical examples that can be deployed horizontally to other departments.
    - Auditors check to see if the presenter is serious about the achievements of his or her own job.

3. *Schedule B*. This is divided into an on-site audit and QC circle presentations. An on-site audit is based on the presidential QC audit Schedule B checklist. In addition, it checks daily data, daily control, and, particularly, proper actions when problems occur as they relate to Schedule A. There are data included on the quality, cost, delivery (Q, C, and D), and human resources for each job area. A list of the records is included so that the auditor's questions can be answered within three seconds. The audit takes from thirty to forty minutes for each section.

A QC circle presents those themes which were recently completed, and the auditor conducts a question and answer period with them.

Plan

1. *Annual schedule*. The presidential audit is determined by an annual schedule and is set three months before the business year being planned has begun. Normally, the company president's schedule is filled up to a year in advance, but the QC audit is participated in voluntarily by the president and will often take up to 44 days of his time. In the past, two to three audits a year were delegated to the vice president or to a senior manager because of other conflicts.

2. *Auditors*. In principle, the auditors include the president as the chief and other senior management. Four people conduct an audit for a relatively large facility such as a plant and two to three people conduct it if the facility is small.

   A group of two auditors can conduct an on-site tour using Schedule B. Each manager is arranged to be an auditor at least twice a year. This arrangement is made by the TQC promotion department head.

3. *Some precautions when selecting dates*. Those units that can be audited in a single day by traveling to and from Tokyo are scheduled independently. Other operating units, such as in the northern island of Hokkaido or the northern Tohoku area, are covered in one continuous trip. The Kansai area is scheduled similarly. This arrangement saves on airline tickets, bullet train tickets, and other travel expenses. However, if employees of these more distant units must work on Saturdays and Sundays, it happens only once or twice a year.

Implementation

1. *Preparation*. One or two weeks before the presidential audit the TQC promotion office head conducts a pre-audit guidance at the request of the unit receiving the audit. This period coincides with producing a summary for Schedule A.

   There, the PDCA for policy, status of companywide horizontal deployment, practical examples, daily control status documents, etc. are summarized and checked both verbally and for data. The work tends to look like preparation for a presentation, but the real aim is on-the-job training and self-reflection on policy by the department and section heads who will be audited, and to check their PDCA work habits.

The president instructs the TQC promotion office head to form good habits by offering pre-audit guidance. Many branch offices can prepare themselves by receiving this pre-audit guidance, so presentations can be better scheduled. These are the purposes, but often errors in data and missing words can be corrected at this time as well.

2. *Department head's audit.* This can be a voluntary audit begun by the head of a department who thinks too much time is being spent in preparing material for the presidential audit. Since it is voluntary, there are no requirements for reporting to the corporate office, nor will it take an entire day.

For example, a branch office checks the status of its policies with the branch office chief and the TQC person in charge. Checking the achievements of the section or group heads and the status of daily control and holding talks with employees makes for a QC-like approach to giving advice. How this check is conducted is really left up to each branch office. But the aim is to avoid a presidential audit for which one is ill-prepared. This also helps to familiarize new employees with QC so that the branch office conducting the check usually comes out with good marks in a QC circle activity evaluation.

3. *The presidential audit.* Each auditor scores each presenter based on the presidential QC audit evaluation chart in Schedule A. Also, improvement points and other noteworthy points are written down.

For Schedule B the scoring is made for each section, but the rest of it is the same as in Schedule A. An auditor might say that the audit is a lot of work, but the summary afterward is even more work.

Improvement points are added to the action plan. Other procedures are regulated according to in-house regulations and the presidential QC audit manual, so that all business offices can follow a standardized procedure.

Evaluation and Follow-Up

1. *Evaluation.* A re-audit is conducted within one month of the audit if the score falls below seventy. The purpose of this is maintenance and improvement of the level of TQC activity that was the subject of the previous Deming Prize challenge. Within our company this is called a "return match," and it is conducted with one to three branch offices in some years. In contrast, branch offices with good scores are awarded with some token award money and their names are carried in the TQC newsletter along with photographs.

Evaluations are made by auditors who are in-house, but every three years or so some branch offices among the 22 are subject to an audit by outside specialists. The purpose of this is to enable all auditors, including the president, to learn about the audit process.

2. *Follow-up.* The results of Schedules A and B audits are recorded in an improvement action plan (presidential QC audit item list), which is submitted to the TQC promotion office. Since all auditors of the presidential QC audit are participants in the TQC promotion office, the improvement plan is confirmed for adequacy. It is then submitted to the president. This improvement plan shows each item with its current status. Attached is a pre- and post-improvement condition report. One of the evaluation tasks of the TQC promotion office is to check for mishandling of some of the items that are thus pointed out.

Conclusion

Five years have passed since the beginning of the presidential audit. What follows is what we have realized as a result of this audit.

There are many employees who do a fine job based on rational data and facts but don't realize that they are following the QC way. Often this work can be made into QC stories and standardized using Schedule B, and can then be deployed horizontally in other departments. This is something we did not initially expect.

The TQC promotion office selects those who will join in next year's QC circle leaders' course. Recently the president said that the QC audit is best when it approves 70 percent of the time and guides only 30 percent of the time.

A QC audit is a rare chance for distant branch offices to have the president look at their work. In this light the audit is also a morale booster. The TQC promotion office plays an important role in this and must have a planned, prioritized approach for promoting TQC.

Our next task is to expand the QC audit to our overseas subsidiaries in eleven foreign countries. Policy deployment and daily control systems were introduced to these overseas subsidiaries about three years ago, but there is still a lot to do. We plan to apply the QC audit system to these subsidiaries beginning in 1983 in order to improve their level of TQC activities.

*   *   *

20

Respecting Others

—Respect others and allow people to exhibit their full potential.

PEOPLE'S NEEDS

One important thing in TQC is to standardize methods properly in order to delegate authority and to allow each and every employee to exhibit his or her full potential.

A. H. Maslow, the industrial psychologist, noted that there are five stages or levels of people's needs, as shown in Figure 20.1. The desires of a higher stage will occur only when the needs of the lower stages are fulfilled. And fulfilling higher-level needs brings greater pleasure.

Physiological Needs

People have physiological desires to satisfy hunger, thirst, sleepiness, and so on. Unless these basic requirements for existence are satisfied, other requirements will not effect human will or action very much. In this kind of situation, most of our will and action will be regulated by these physiological desires.

The Need for Stability and Safety

Once the physiological needs are fulfilled, the desire for stability and safety, which is the next stage of desire, will be heightened. This can be translated as the desire to keep away from danger, threat, pain, or worry, and to assure continuity for tomorrow and one's future safety.

Social Needs

Once the need for safety and stability is satisfied to a degree, social needs become dominant. These are the desires for acceptance by others both individually and collectively, for recognition, for love, for friendship. This means

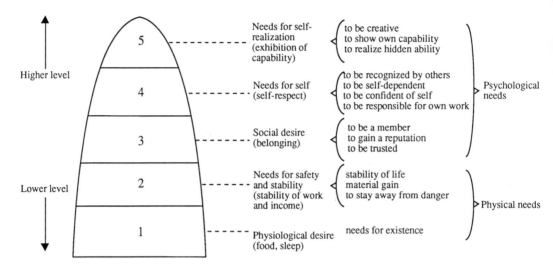

FIGURE 20.1.   Five stages of human needs.

both giving and receiving. When these desires become strong, they will affect people in various ways and produce various actions. The interesting human relations in a factory are a result of this.

Needs of Self

Next the needs of the self grow strong. These are the desires for self-respect and for reputation. People want recognition for their capabilities. They want to be evaluated properly for their work. They want to be consulted when decisions are made. These desires are quite dominant among people in advanced countries, and our actions and awareness are formed on the basis of fulfilling them.

Need for Self-Realization

Once the desire for self is satisfied to a degree, the need for self-realization becomes dominant. This is the desire to improve one's latent abilities, to learn and to grow, to be more creative.

Summary

The above hierarchy of needs indicates that trying to teach people who are governed by the lower-level needs by attempting to motivate their sense of creativity and higher-level needs will not produce a great effect.

RESPECTING HUMAN NATURE

One of the basics of TQC is respect for human nature. Respecting human nature means to respect and emphasize humane ways and to exhibit humane characteristics to the fullest. TQC activities are those that appreciate people's emotions, and allow people to exhibit their wisdom, creativity, judgment, planning ability, action, and guidance to the greatest extent possible. Because humans are animals with emotions, people doing the same kind of work can end up with different results and efficiency depending on their attitudes toward their work.

The way in which we work generally reflects Maslow's two higher-level needs: for self-respect and for self-realization.

A workplace that exudes vitality is one where human nature is respected and human abilities are promoted. Conditions that produce a positive attitude toward work include:

- A clear purpose and target for the job
- A clear delegation of authority to the level where the work is done so that one can act on one's own responsibility
- The ability to devise and to try one's own work methods
- The opportunity to know the results of one's work

Human relations are poor and morale is low in a workplace where human nature is neglected because of the pursuit of higher productivity or zero defects. Order and regimentation are emphasized when human nature is viewed as being evil. But where the goodness of human nature is emphasized and good communication is established regarding targets, standards, and work methods, including all work from top to bottom, the efficiency of the work and the morale of the people are high.

QC CIRCLE ACTIVITIES

One of the features of TQC in Japan is this respect for human nature. QC circle activities are what make this feature more concrete and produce the results.

In "QC circle general principles"[13] a QC circle is defined generally as:

- a small group (6 to 8 people)
- in same work area (group is formed by foreman and workers together)
- perform QC activities (for achievement of 5 major tasks of work area—quality, cost, delivery, safety, human relations)
- voluntary (not ordered to participate but do so voluntarily)

This "small group" involves:

- participation by all (participation, attendance, speaking up, work-sharing for good or bad, by all)
- continuity (not hit-or-miss, but continued into job area)
- through self-motivation and mutual motivation (study by oneself and motivating each other)
- by use of QC techniques (use of easy and effective "7 QC Tools")
- as a part of companywide QC activities (achieve the role assigned to the front line of the job by sharing a portion of TQC)
- performs control and improvement of job area (major purposes of QC circle activity are control—maintaining existing quality level—and improving the level)

The basic aims of QC circle activities are to:

1. Contribute to the company's overall structural improvement and development
2. Respect human nature and create a meaningful workplace
3. Bring forth human capabilities to the fullest extent

Number (3) above relates to the individual. People have endless capabilities. They are different from machines. Therefore, as one motivates oneself and learns, one becomes mentally motivated and one's capabilities develop further. Number (2) above relates to the job or work area. QC circle activities view people as human beings and respect their human nature. They emphasize self-motivation and creativity. As a result, human relationships in the workplace are improved and the workplace becomes a meaningful and pleasant environment. Number (1) above relates to the company. The company becomes more modern and its structures improve so as to promote expansion when QC circles are well-established as the core of QC activities. This is because actions become more voluntary, views become wider, and opinions become more well-founded and constructive. The following ideas are included in this basic concept.

- The growth of each individual
- Respect for human nature
- Improved human relationships
- Activities that make one's work more enjoyable
- Activities that make one's work easier

INTRODUCTION OF QC CIRCLES AT THE SANWA BANK, LTD.

The Sanwa Bank, Ltd. has its corporate offices in Osaka. Its capital is approximately 111.4 billion yen and it employs approximately 18,000 persons. In terms of deposited funds, it ranks fifth in the nation.

This bank introduced QC circles in the spring of 1977, and was the first bank to do so. Mr. T. Akashi (the present chairman of the board) describes the reason for introducing QC circles at Sanwa Bank as follows. The following is a portion of a special speech on his experiences with QC circles,[4c] presented at the Second QC Circle International Conference held on September 3, 1981.

* * *

As I look back there may have been three reasons for our introducing QC circles at Sanwa Bank. Number one was related to my management philosophy. I had become chairman about a year before, in April of 1976, and introduced QC circles because I had always thought that we should have a management that respects people. My idea of bank management is to make the job more worthwhile and create a pleasant work environment. The harder our employees train, the more our appreciation of them grows and the more they continue to improve. We want our employees to be able to look back on their time with Sanwa Bank as a fruitful period in their lives, full of pleasant memories. I wanted management to have this goal, which I call "managing with respect for people," and I emphasized this in my first speech as chairman.

The second reason was a search for some meaningful project to commemorate the 100th anniversary of our bank in 1977. I had distributed to all the bank branches our slogan, "Let's do our best to be kind to others; let's warm our spirit; let's train our minds and improve our knowledge." This was at the start of 1977 and was an action guideline for our daily work.

Normally we would ask our customers how they would like to celebrate a bank anniversary. But I wanted to respond to their contribution with something especially meaningful. Thus, we were looking for a project that no other bank had ever taken up to make our anniversary a memorable one.

Third, I always wanted our bank to be the people's bank, something different from the others. We had a plan that was called Operation Clover. It was a five-year, long-term business plan aimed at achieving the goal of becoming a people's bank. We were looking at how we could respond to diversifying customer needs, what services we could offer, and how to develop our employees, who were really the basis for all of this. As a result of this research, I discovered that the basic idea of QC circles and a customer-oriented quality control spirit agreed with my management philosophy of respect for people. That is why I decided to introduce QC circle activities into all of our branches. This was certainly a worthwhile commemorative to our 100th year.

Since then, Sanwa Bank has been expanding its QC circle activities, and at present (March 1984), we have the following:

- Number of circles: approximately 2,300
- Nonmanagerial participants: approximately 12,000
- Themes that have been solved: approximately 39,000 (averaging 17 case studies per circle)
- Items proposed at circles: approximately 38,000 (average of 16.5 per circle)

*   *   *

HOW TO START AND RUN A QC CIRCLE

How to Start a QC Circle

The introduction of a QC circle can differ depending on the type of industry, the mode, and the circumstances. What follows is a general-purpose method.

How to Start a QC Circle

Step 1. *Look at other QC circles*. The leaders or promoters of QC circles often visit other companies or other job areas where circles are already in place. Or they may attend QC circle conferences or exchange meetings.

Step 2. *Listen to QC circle stories*. Attend seminars or speeches given at the QC circle headquarters of JUSE or the Japan Standards Association, and learn about the basics of QC circles and how they are administered.

Step 3. *Read QC circle books*. Read and learn from QC circle general principles, *Basics of QC Circle Activity Administration* or the *SQC Monthly* (all published by JUSE) as a start.

Step 4. *Talk to many people*. Talk to people who are interested in QC circles and then talk with the head of a company promoting QC circles for guidance and instruction.

Step 5. *Try it out*. Form a QC circle with a supervisor of a job area as the leader and try it out.

Step 6. *Reflect on the results*. The way the meeting was held, the role sharing, the discussion of themes, the use of techniques, problem solution, etc. should be reflected upon by all members.

Criteria for Running a QC Circle

The following conditions must be created in order to run a QC circle:

1. The leader must understand the basics of QC circle operation (see Figure 20.2).
2. Let members of the QC circle feel the need for such activities.

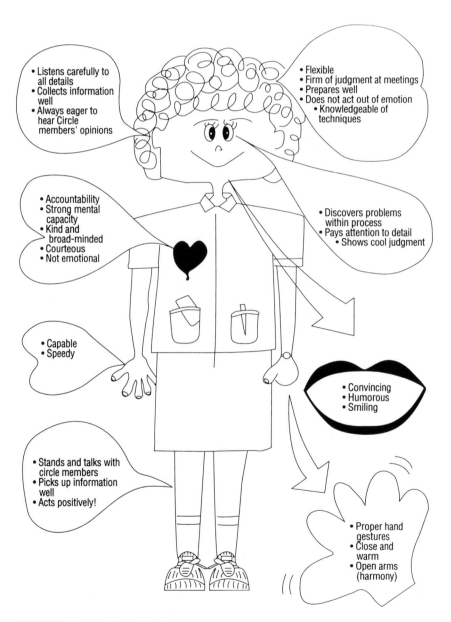

FIGURE 20.2. The ideal QC circle leader.

3. Let members become positive about doing it.

4. Form an environment that fosters voluntary participation.

5. Set targets and perform actions to achieve them.

6. Learn about other QC techniques for which the QC circle is a tool.

7. Stress action.

8. Evaluate the QC circle activities (self-evaluation or by one's boss).

How to Run a QC Circle

It does not always go smoothly from the beginning. Normally, trial-and-error occurs. Therefore, everyone in the circle should join together to find the best way to run the circle. Leadership and teamwork are necessary. For good teamwork, awareness by all the members of the meaning of the QC circle, their attitudes towards it, and their understanding of the effects of dialogue and communication and joint action toward a common goal, are important. QC circle activities are administered in the following way.

How To Administer a QC Circle

Step 1. *Formation.* The supervisor of the job area becomes a leader with his subordinates as the members of the QC circle. They receive approval from their boss.

Step 2. *Registration.* As soon as possible after its formation, register the circle with the in-house QC circle office or QC circle headquarters (JUSE). This makes the circle more responsible.

Step 3. *Set themes.* Listen to company policy or to the opinions of your boss and select a theme that is appropriate.

Step 4. *Prepare a plan of action.* Make a plan of action for the theme and get approval from the boss.

Step 5. *Carry out the QC circle activities.* Take specific actions for improvement and control based on QC circle meetings and morning or evening meetings. Keep a record of QC circle activities. QC circle leaders should occasionally get together to discuss problems and solutions.

    1. Collect data on problems and analyze them using the 7 QC Tools.

    2. Devise and create ways to achieve improvement.

    3. Carry out the improvement and confirm the results.

    4. If the improvement is achieved, maintain it.

Step 6. *Check progress.* Record the performance and check progress and results. Report to your boss and ask for guidance.

Step 7. *Summarize the results in a report.* This report of results is reported to one's boss.

Step 8. *Present the results at a QC circle conference.* Presentation of results is often possible at in-house QC meetings, and exceptionally good ones can be presented at outside meetings for external evaluation.

Step 9. *Look for new themes.* Evaluate and reflect on past results in order to determine the next activities. QC circles stay within the job area to select their next theme and to continue their activities.

"QC CIRCLE ACTIVITIES AND ME": THE EXPERIENCE OF A QUALITY HOMEMAKER

This next essay is from Mrs. R. Matsumoto, a homemaker and an employee in the electrolysis section of Shin-Etsu-Nittsu-Ko Company. This company makes telephones and capacitors. She has spent seventeen years with the company and has two years of experience in the QC circle. The title of her paper is "QC Circles: Encounters of a Great Kind."

This essay was selected from 585 that were solicited by QC circle head-quarters in 1981 for the 1,000th QC Circle Conference. The title of the conference was "QC Circle Activities and Me."[14]

The story is about a housewife who participates in a QC circle at the same time that she manages her and her family's home life, which she enjoys very much. The story of her personal growth is very impressive.

*   *   *

My third-grade son came up to me and said, "Mom, you work so hard, I think I want to be just like you." This was after I had begun studying at home for our QC circle, and it convinced me even more to show my children by example rather than just pressuring them to study and study. I was pleasantly surprised to learn that QC circle activities were not only effective at the workplace and for maintaining quality and improving productivity, but could also be used in the home.

It was about two years ago that QC circles were introduced to our company, in June of 1978. At the morning meeting there was an explanation stating that the company was introducing QC circles. They encouraged us to be positive about it. The problem was that the term "QC" was new to me and I had difficulty understanding it.

After six months my boss said that there were too many members in my section's QC circle and so we needed to reorganize it. First the supervisor nominated a circle leader. Leaders were to be selected from among circle members who had achieved their targets. The component assembly circle had Mrs. X as its leader, and the final finishing QC circle had Mrs. Y as its leader. Suddenly my name was called and boy, was I surprised! I said to myself, "Oh, how could I be so unlucky?" But the real problems were to come only later.

A training meeting was held every day after work for QC circle leaders, particularly to study Pareto charts, cause-and-effect diagrams, histograms, and the other 7 QC Tools. We also learned to calculate square roots and sigma. This was all very hard for me because I had never gone past the ninth grade. Everything was so new to me that I was lost. Our section head, who was the instructor, asked, "Do we all understand?"

I decided to study at home because I did not want to drop out. In the eighteen years since I had finished school I had kept telling myself to work as honestly as I could and to do what I was told to. I never thought that I would be back at school again. Studying at home for me was like a war every day. This was because, in addition to working, I am a homemaker and a mother of two children.

After a day's hard work and my chores at home, including putting my kids to bed, it was a real struggle to want to study. Often I fell asleep with pencil in hand. I even almost gave up a few times. What kept me going was the cooperation that I received at home. My husband came to pick me up if studying at the company kept me late, and my mother-in-law often cooked for me. And everyone waited to eat until I came home.

The idea of QC was strange for our in-laws at the beginning, but nowadays they keep encouraging me to keep at it. Many of the themes that we set out to achieve were accomplished.

We were first in our in-house presentation meetings and our circle was selected as the best. We were then chosen to participate in the 836th QC Circle Women's Conference (Nagano Area, Kanto Branch). We worked until very late at night preparing for it, with the cooperation of all members and the advice of our bosses. We were not really ready for it, but we went ahead anyway and attended the conference. I was surprised that many of the attendees were so young, in their twenties, because I, being in my thirties, was almost a grandmother to them. After the conference our boss, who is usually quite strict about things, congratulated us with a warm thank-you and other encouragement.

QC circle activity needs the cooperation of all members. Being a homemaker or a beginner is no excuse. Everyone must work hard and think hard. Sometimes a "people problem" pops up, which makes us all sad. But perseverance, with good will and sincerity, wins out in the end. This is the one lesson we have learned from our QC circle experience. I will never forget the good feeling of working together, of being honest with each other, reaching for a common goal. QC circles have not only reduced the number of rejects and helped us achieve our goals, but they also have made for better human relationships on which better results and further achievement of goals can be realized. This is my opinion. Our bosses told us that the *result* is everything and that effort alone is not evaluated. But I believe that an accumulation of daily efforts changes impossibilities into possibilities. I believe that I should strive further for better QC circle activities in order to repay my family's wonderful kindness and cooperation. My encounter with the QC circle has made my life wonderful.

*   *   *

Bibliography

1. "Deming Prize, Abstracts, Japan QC Award Reporting Speeches," Deming Prize Committee, JUSE.
   a. "Abstracts, 1983 Deming Prize Report"
   b. "Abstracts, 1982 Deming Prize Report"
   c. "Abstracts, 1981 Deming Prize Report"
   d. "Abstracts, 1980 Deming Prize Report"
   e. "Abstracts, 1979 Deming Prize Report"

2. *QC Magazine*, JUSE.
   a. Shimomura, H., "Quality data from market—mainly of department stores," Vol. 30, No. 9, pp. 12–17, 1979.
   b. Tsukamoto, T., and T. Murata, "Use of market quality information at design department," Vol. 32, June Special Issue, pp. 130–34, 1981.
   c. Hosotani, K., "Use of statistical methods—its significance and methods," Vol. 32, No. 4, pp. 6–9, 1981.
   d. Fukuoka, M., "Process capability improvement by use of QC chart," Vol. 30, May Special Issue, pp. 90–95, 1979.
   e. Shiraishi, S., and N. Tsubouchi, "Evaluation of external spray finishing material—extraction of evaluation items and method of evaluation," Vol. 34, Nov. Special Issue, pp. 88–92, 1983.
   f. Mori, K., "Failure analysis on valve spring for fuel injection pump," Vol. 33, June Special Issue, pp. 252–55, 1982.
   g. "QC Terminologies," Vol. 34, No. 10, pp. 86–87, 1983.
   h. Nuizima, K., and M. Sasaki, "QC approach for design/work stage at Kajima Construction Company—for the development of large PC low temperature tank," Vol. 34, No. 6, pp. 49–55, 1983.
   i. Mizuno, Y., "TQC promotion and QC education of department/section heads at purchasing department of Toyota Jidosha Company," Vol. 34, No. 7, pp. 22–26, 1983.
   j. Tarumi, K., "QC education of department/section heads at Yaskawa-Denki Company," Vol. 34, No. 7, pp. 45–50, 1983.
   k. Ikezawa, T., "Policy deployment," Vol. 30, No. 12, pp. 6–7, 1979.

l. Hirakawa, T., "Policy deployment at Ricoh Company," Vol. 33, No. 9, pp. 18–23, 1982.

m. Shimada, Z., "Administration of presidential QC audit at Pentel Company," Vol. 30, No. 12, pp. 40–44, 1982.

3. *TQC Magazine*, JUSE.
   a. Hirashita, K., "Case (2), Let us build quality in processes," No. 200, pp. 17–19, 1979.
      Koiso, M., "Case (3), Let us eliminate customers' complaints," No. 200, pp. 20–23, 1979.
   b. Hosotani, K., "How to collect data—to talk with data," No. 248, pp. 4–12, 1983.
   c. _____, "Improvement Case (2), Improvement of V-belt adjustment work," No. 133, pp. 15–19, 1974.
   d. _____, "Importance of and key to factor analysis—to find real cause," No. 243, pp. 4–6, 1983.
   e. Work standard seminar, subcommittee. "Seminar No. 1, Aim of Work Standards," No. 170, pp. 78–85, 1977.

4. "Quality Monthly Text," Quality Monthly Committee publ.
   a. Kusaba, I., ed., "Management and QC," No. 93, p. 12, 1977.
   b. Toyoda, M., "Quality Company—management and practice of quality," No. 101, pp. 4–6, 1978.
   c. Akashi, T., "QC circle activity and me," No. 135, pp. 3–9, 1982.
   d. Hosotani, K., "QC way of viewing and thinking," No. 129, 1981.

5. *Business Week*, March 12, 1979.

6. *QC Magazine* edit. comm., ed., "For department/section heads—future company and quality," pp. 137–43, JUSE Press, 1977.

7. Kawano, G., "QA for product planning," "QA for mature product planning—plan development of shavers," 37th QC Symposium, p. 70, JUSE, 1983.

8. "QC implementation instruction," JUSE, 1984.

9. Abstracts, "Experiences 1425th QC circle conference (Tokuyama)," pp. 36–37, JUSE, 1984.

10. Hosotani, K., "QC techniques for the shop floor (advanced)," 100Q100A Series, No. 6, pp. 72–73, JUSE Press, 1978.

11. Mizuno, S., and Y. Akao, eds., Quality function deployment, JUSE Press, 1978.

12. Shimoyamada, K., "Control by function for QA," *Quality*, Vol. 14, No. 4, 1984.

13. QC Circle HQ, ed., "QC circle general principles," JUSE, 1970.

14. QC Circle HQ, ed., "QC circle activities and me," 1,000th QC Circle Conference, Essays, pp. 41–45, JUSE, 1981.

15. Ishikawa, K., ''Japanese QC,'' JUSE Press, 1981.

16. Mizuno, S., supv., QC technique development department, ed., ''New 7 Tools of QC for Managers and Staff,'' JUSE Press, 1979.

17. Hosotani, K., ''7 Tools of QC—Easy QC Technique Exercise,'' JUSE Press, 1982.

Index